4-

D1483575

THE WANDERING ALBATROSS

1. The greatest sea-bird in the world

THE WANDERING ALBATROSS

WILLIAM JAMESON

With drawings by Peter Shepheard

I now belong to the higher cult of mortals
for I have seen the albatross!
ROBERT CUSHMAN MURPHY, *Logbook for Grace*

RUPERT HART-DAVIS
SOHO SQUARE LONDON
1958

Printed in Great Britain by Richard Clay and Company, Ltd.,
Bungay, Suffolk

For E. and F.

CONTENTS

PHOTOGRAPHS

ACKNOWLEDGEMENTS

Frontispiece and plates 6 & 7	H.R.H. The Duke of Edinburgh
Plate 2	Commander R. N. Everett, R.N.
Plate 3	Admiral Sir Caspar John
Plates 4 (*a*) & 4 (*i*)	Reverend Eric Milner, R.N.
Plates 8, 9, 10 & 11	Captain J. V. Wilkinson, R.N. and Leading Airman J. Clayton
Plates 12 & 14	Dr André Migot
Plates 13 & 21	Dr L. Harrison Matthews
Plates 17, 18, 19, 20, 22 & 23	Lieut.-Colonel Niall Rankin

Plate 26 is from a drawing by E. H. Werner originally published in 1857

MAPS AND DIAGRAMS

Diagrams on pages 29, 71 and 93 drawn by Peter Shepheard;
others by K. C. Jordan. The diagrams on pages 68 and 69 are
based on graphs by Commander H. C. N. Goodhart, R.N.

PREFACE

No one who has seen the Wandering Albatross suddenly appearing in a remote part of the loneliest seas in the world will ever
forget the experience. In November 1940 the German pocket
battleship *Graf Spee* had sunk a small merchant ship off
Madagascar, and then disappeared. She might have gone east
into the Indian Ocean or doubled back into the South Atlantic.
The ship in which I was serving had been ordered to take
up a strategic position south of the Cape to cover either even-
tuality, but the seas around remained empty. It was weary,
monotonous work, and when the great white bird came sailing across the wake one evening it was a heart-lifting event.
Where had the albatross come from? How did it live? The
navigating officer's copy of W. B. Alexander's *Birds of the Ocean*
supplied some of the answers to the questions we were asking,
but this book covers all the ocean birds, and cannot give many
details. Later I started to assemble information about the greatest sea-bird in the world. The search was more difficult than
I had anticipated, for most of it was included in books and
reports covering a great variety of other subjects.

I believe that I have mentioned all the more important facts
about *Diomedea exulans*, but even today there are many gaps in
our knowledge of a bird which is found in remote parts of the
ocean, ranges over millions of square miles and breeds only
on a handful of rarely visited islands.

Watching birds and learning how they tackle the problem of
existence is a wonderful antidote to the strains and stresses of
our modern world. Few birds have more interesting habits
than the Wandering Albatross; indeed it is in many ways
unique.

WILLIAM JAMESON

Hoveton St. Peter.
July 1957.

ACKNOWLEDGMENTS

I AM most grateful to the members of the staff of the Bird Room and of the General and Zoological Libraries of the British Museum (Natural History). In particular I wish to thank Mr M. J. Rowland and Mr F. Sawyer, who produced invaluable books and papers with very little help from references.

I have listed the sources used in the Bibliography, but I wish to record my special indebtedness to the works of Dr Robert Cushman Murphy of the American Museum of Natural History, Dr Lionel Harrison Matthews, the Scientific Director of the Zoological Society, and Lieut-Colonel Niall Rankin.

A book of this sort is greatly dependent on its illustrations. It was a lucky day for me when Mr Peter Shepheard decided to undertake the task. His delightful pictures speak for themselves.

It is not easy to photograph the Wandering Albatross, particularly at sea. The bird is not shy, but it flies fast and the weather conditions over most of its range are frequently very disagreeable. I have been lucky to be able to use the work of several Antarctic travellers to supplement my own indifferent efforts.

His Royal Highness The Duke of Edinburgh took the photographs, which appear as a frontispiece and in two other places, from H.M. Royal Yacht *Britannia* during his world tour in 1956–57 and has graciously consented to allow me to use them.

Vice-Admiral Sir Conolly Abel Smith, and Captain John Adams, R.N., of Her Majesty's Yacht, took a personal interest in collecting information for me, and it was through the former that the photographs taken by officers and ratings serving in H.M.S. *Protector* came my way. Captain J. V. Wilkinson, R.N., of that ship also, supplied some interesting notes on birds observed ashore in South Georgia, and the coloured slides of photographs taken by the Reverend Eric Milner of birds following the *Protector* have been valuable to Mr Shepheard and to me. The comprehensive series of photographs of the nesting and courting procedure were taken by Colonel Niall Rankin, Dr Harrison Matthews and Leading Airman J. Clayton. My thanks are due to Messrs Collins and to Messrs MacGibbon and Kee for allowing me to reproduce the photographs which were first published in *Antarctic Isle* (Rankin) and *Wandering Albatross* (Matthews).

Commander H. C. N. Goodhart, R.N., one of the foremost glider pilots of our day, with the knowledge of aeronautics and meteorology which this implies, has kindly read my chapter on flight. I have incorporated various valuable suggestions made by him. He also drew the graphs which appear as Figs. 2 and 3.

Finally I wish to acknowledge the help and advice of Mr Richard Garnett of Rupert Hart-Davis Ltd.

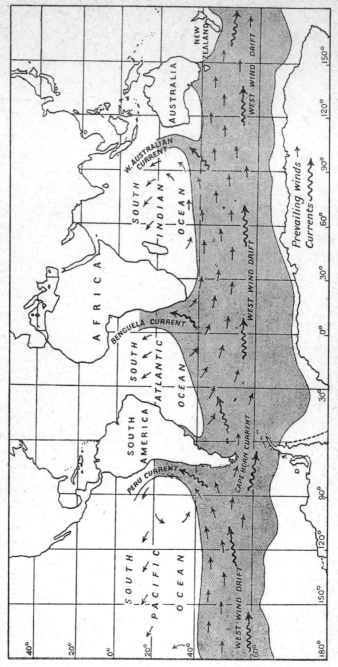

THE ALBATROSS LATITUDES

1. *The Long-Anticipated Bird*

November 23. Mid-ocean. St Helena was below the horizon when we passed nearby two days ago. When I looked at the chart this evening Africa was 800 miles to port, South America three times as far to starboard and there was no land ahead but the far-distant, frozen wastes of Antarctica. We are steaming S.S.E. through very empty waters. No birds, no flying fish, no dolphins or whales. The sky has been overcast and grey and the sea lifeless and dull. The wind, such as it is, blows fitfully from no particular direction, for we are in the Horse Latitudes, between the South-east Trades and the Westerlies. I have travelled far to see the greatest sea-bird in the world, but must wait for a few days longer. Wandering Albatrosses have rarely been seen below the tropic of Capricorn, and we are still some distance from the northernmost limit of their ordinary range.

November 24. We were directly under the sun at noon in 19° S. and almost exactly on the meridian of Greenwich. I spent several hours on deck searching the surrounding sea, without much hope of success. Tomorrow we enter the edge of the Benguela Current, which flows northward from the Southern

Ocean along the western shores of South Africa. We will then pass from a barren to a fertile area; from water supporting little life to one rich in the minute organisms known collectively as plankton.

Sea-water is not a homogeneous substance. Like soil it varies in composition and in its capacity to support life. "Fertile" sea-water is rich in diatoms—minute plants which grow in the sun-lit upper layers of the ocean and are the basis of all marine life. Diatoms are the pasture of the sea, and upon them graze billions of small creatures such as the euphasians—the opossum shrimps or "krill" which are the food of fishes, birds and mammals, including the largest sorts of whales. A Swedish scientist, voyaging near the Cape nearly 200 years ago, graphically described the small organisms upon which all else depends. Ships' decks were closer to the sea in those days, and progress through it less regular. Travellers had more time to think, and greater leisure to observe. Peering down through the milky-blue water, Sparr-man suddenly realised that he was looking at something so full of tiny objects that it was, quite literally, alive.

A thick mass several fathoms deep . . . a small corner of the sea . . . afforded nourishment to more animals at once, than perhaps are to be found on the whole face of the earth. This opened to me a door, if I may be allowed the expression, to nature's copious store-house in the deep; so that at one hasty view I could get a glimpse of that amazing superfluity, which feeds millions of fishes, and at the same time lines the inside of the whale, that great Colossus of the deep, with that oily fatness with which it abounds. . . . It was these insects that the fat sea-lions and seals, diving and amphibious fowls, many kinds of albatrosses, together with sea-gulls of all sorts, were in quest of.*

The facts are vividly expressed. The Southern Ocean, amazingly rich in plankton, can support a vast population of pelagic creatures. Currents caused by the wind, the difference in density of warm and cold water and other factors have made the

* Anders Sparrman, *A Voyage to the Cape of Good Hope towards the Antarctic Polar Circle and Round the World*, 1786.

boundaries of the fertile areas, the sub-Antarctic and Antarctic zones, almost as distinct and clear as those which, on shore, separate moorland from fruitful valley.

November 25. Noon position 24° S., 6° E. We have left the tropics astern. The air is fresher, the sea bluer and the wind comes steadily from the west, fulfilling one of the necessary conditions for the great bird's presence, for the albatross "sails"— as dependent on the wind for sustained motion as ships before the days of steam. Its great wings are perfectly adapted for gliding and soaring, but its breast-muscles are comparatively small. The albatross cannot flap for extended periods and uses the wind to search the ocean for its living. Its normal life-zone must be windy as well as rich in food. A wind-map of the southern hemisphere superimposed on a map of its cold currents will give a good idea where Wandering Albatrosses will be found.

November 26. 29° 17′ S. at noon today. All the pundits give 30 degrees south latitude as the northern border of the albatross's range, so I knew that at any moment my patience might be rewarded and the long-anticipated bird glide into sight.

It was a beautiful day, cool and fresh. The sun was shining and a biggish swell swept by from the south-west; the water was deep blue, sparkling and alive, and the wave-tops creamy white. During the night we had crossed one of the great ocean boundaries—between the sub-tropical and sub-Antarctic zones. The temperature of the sea dropped quite suddenly by several degrees and an analysis of the water would have revealed a higher proportion of nitrogenous compounds and other nutritious substances on which plankton thrives. We have left the semi-arid waters of the tropical and sub-tropical zones and have entered the fertile regions of abundant life. I thought of a flight over southern California. After passing for miles over yellow, arid hills we suddenly came to irrigated country, fruitful and green.

I spent most of the morning on deck, but saw no birds, though several times schools of porpoises went by—curving clear of the surface and sliding back into the sea with scarcely a splash. These waters are *alive*—quite different from the torpid stuff further north. Several people were keeping a look-out for me and a message, reporting a big, white bird on the starboard beam, brought me scurrying on deck this afternoon. It must have been the flash of a breaking wave, for I could see nothing else. It seems strange to look for a bird in the middle of the ocean, hundreds of miles from land. The great majority of our British sea-birds are shore-based, returning daily to some part of the coast. When we sight an albatross it will have been at sea for at least four months, and very possibly (if a young non-breeding bird) for one, two or even three years, and for the whole of this period it has probably been out of sight of land. Land, except at nesting time, does not enter into the albatross's scheme of things. They are as much creatures of the sea as any fish; truly pelagic.

At four o'clock I had given up hope of seeing an albatross and was in the wardroom having a cup of tea and idly turning the dog-eared pages of a month-old *Illustrated London News*. The ship, with the sea abeam, rolled gently to the long swell. At the end of the table two messmates were playing a not-too-serious game of chess. Someone was gently strumming on our long-suffering piano and someone else, standing beside him at the open scuttle, was gazing over the ever-moving ocean rustling by. Suddenly he said, "Gosh, what a bird! Is that what you are looking for?"

I sprang to his side, just in time to catch a glimpse of a great bird skimming over the waves a quarter of a mile away. Body and wings made a white cross as it banked almost vertically and disappeared from view. I ran up echoing steel ladders to the deck and saw the bird again, much further off now, on rigid, motionless wings skimming close above the water. It turned into the wind, soared up 40 or 50 feet, banked towards us and swooped down to pass across the wake 100 yards astern. So high was its speed that in a few seconds it was far away; hidden altogether as it followed the trough of the swell; a flashing white cross against the deep blue sea as it banked and rose. For an hour or more I remained on deck, but although the albatross stayed in sight it did not come close to us again. Finally it settled on the water and disappeared astern. The sun sank lower, twilight turned into dusk, but the bird had left us.

November 26. Just above my bunk a single scuttle faces out on the ship's quarter. Our course was S.S.W., and when I woke the rising sun was low on the port beam. On the white-painted deck overhead, light reflected off the sea cast a disc of mottled brightness which slid to and fro with the gentle rolling of the ship. I lay for a while listening to the familiar noises of distant machinery. Every now and again a bigger lurch made the glass on my washstand clink. It was very comfortable in my warm bunk and I was loath to move, but finally I sat up and looked out. Immediately I was broad awake, for the albatross was back again.

The bird I had seen the day before was an old male Wandering Albatross, pure white except for his jet-black wing-tips. This was the same bird, or one whose plumage was strikingly similar. The ship was steaming at 17 knots, but the bird must have been moving through the air at about three times this speed, for it had no difficulty in returning at regular intervals to a position on our quarter after covering an ellipse which took it far out abeam and astern. Yet this high-speed flight seemed absolutely effortless. As it banked, soared and dived it trimmed its great wings very slightly, but that was all.

The bird remained with us all day, usually following the same undulating track whose nearest arc passed directly over our wake. When the galley refuse was ditched, at breakfast time and again around noon, it settled on the water to feed on fancied tit-bits, floating very high so that we could see it bobbing about a long way off astern, before it was hidden by the waves. In half an hour or so it was back again.

Even in an age that attaches great importance to records it is not the size of the Wandering Albatross which makes it so re-markable. The never-ending source of wonder is the extra-ordinary ease of its flight—a bird as big as a swan and weighing perhaps 20 pounds, which swims through the air as readily as a trout in a quiet pool. Long ago they christened it the monarch of ocean birds. As J. F. Green wrote in 1887—

no one who has watched [an albatross] following a ship in open water, its broad white breast and enormous spread of wing outlined clearly against the glorious blue of the sky as it soars over the taffrail, will be disposed to question its right to the title.*

It is the largest surviving flying creature, though its dimensions have often been exaggerated. W. B. Alexander † states that the span of the wings is said occasionally to reach 14 feet, and C. Parkinson, writing in the *Cornhill Magazine* for May 1900 on the great birds of the Southern Ocean, went one better with a reference to a gigantic specimen in the Sydney Museum with a spread of 17 feet 6 inches. Well-authenticated data do not bear out these figures, but the facts are sufficiently remarkable. A large number, accurately measured, gave a tip-to-tip dimen-sion averaging just over 10 feet; very big ones, invariably males, running up to 12 feet. The length from tip to tail is about 4 feet. Weights up to 26¾ pounds for a male and 20¾ pounds for a female have been recorded, but 18 to 20 pounds would be a good average.

By sunset our albatross had come with us for 200 miles that day and must have covered two or three times that distance in the process. The albatross, more than any other bird, has the habit of following ships. It would be nice to think that they crave company in the loneliness of the ocean, but the facts are more prosaic. Scraps thrown overboard make a pleasant change, and their usual diet of squids and shrimps is brought conveniently to the surface by the turbulence of a passing vessel's wake.

They are surface feeders, never diving for their food, but will

* *Ocean Birds.*   † *Birds of the Ocean,* 1928.

swoop down at anything floating on the water, particularly if its colour is white. This accounts for, but does not entirely explain, a surprising find in the stomach of a bird taken in a desolate part of the ocean, by Dr E. A. Wilson of the *Discovery*— "An undigested Roman Catholic tract with a portrait of Cardinal Vaughan." *

This habit of swooping at objects on the water has earned for the albatross an evil reputation. The famous naturalist John Gould (1848) † refers to the "ferocious disposition of the albatross" and repeats the allegation that they will fearlessly attack a drowning man. Corbett's *Naval Operations* ‡ describes how in the First World War the boats from the British cruiser *Kent*, lowered to pick up survivors from the German cruiser *Nürnberg* after the battle of the Falkland Islands, found albatrosses attacking "even the living." Nevertheless, on their nesting sites their disposition is particularly amiable. Quite without fear of man, they are not in the least aggressive and can be approached and even handled with impunity. The albatross is voracious rather than ferocious, though for a man swimming in the sea it comes to much the same thing, for the great hooked beak, with razor-sharp sides, is a fearsome weapon. There is the very circumstantial account § of an incident involving a man who fell overboard from a sailing-ship bound for Australia. An albatross swooped down and made a peck at him, but the sailor seized his assailant by the neck, held its head under water until the bird had drowned, and used its buoyant body as a float. The man was wearing sea-boots and oilskins, which greatly hampered his movements, the sea was very rough and it was an hour before he was picked up, but with the help of his unusual lifebuoy he returned on board smiling, "apparently none the worse for his unexpected immersion." History does not relate what subsequently happened to the seaman, but I suspect he

* Edward A. Wilson, *Aves*, Vol. II, 1907.
† *The Birds of Australia.*
‡ Sir Julian S. Corbett, *History of the Great War*, Vol. I, 1920.
§ *Sydney Morning Herald*, 24 October 1881.

died in his bed at a ripe old age. The albatross was the first the ship had sighted for a month!

November 27. Three albatrosses in company this morning, one of which looked uncommonly like our old white friend. The other two were younger birds, mostly white below but speckled or brown-black above—"Leopard Goneys" as the whalers used to call them. If the old bird has really been with us for two and a half days he has covered 1,000 miles on a direct line in our company. Do they fly on through the night? A Captain C. C. Dixon who served for twenty-seven years in sail and covered 250,000 miles in the albatross latitudes is an unusually reliable authority, for he made a hobby of observing birds and kept a careful record of what he saw. Dixon is sure that albatrosses fly on moonlight nights, but never observed them when there was no moon, even though it was clear enough to see so great a bird against the starlit sky. Yet a ship may travel 100 to 200 miles in the hours of darkness and the albatrosses are with her at daylight. That the same, and not just a similar bird is present has been proved by noting peculiarities in plumage, broken feathers and other distinctive features.* Most convincing of all, perhaps, is the fact that albatrosses remain in company throughout the twenty-four hours of the virtually continuous daylight of summer in high southern latitudes. How then do they rest?

Old Salts have unblushingly affirmed that the albatross sleeps out the middle watches on the yard-arm! † It has frequently been said that they "sleep on the wing." More likely sleep, as we know it, is unnecessary except at long intervals. Their flight is so effortless that they can rest in the air, just as a crane, poised on one leg, head under wing, continues to balance itself whilst "asleep." Albatrosses "grounded" by calm weather can certainly be seen asleep on the water, heads folded on their back in the same restful position which they adopt when brood-

* The bird in the lower plate opposite, easily distinguishable by its white-tipped inner primaries, was with H.M.S. *York* for 4 days. Speed of the ship 18 knots.

† Their three toes face forward; they cannot possibly perch.

Against the bright blue sky (2) and the dark blue sea (3). Both birds flying just above stalling speed. Note small under-wing feathers displaced by turbulence (*top*) and wing coverts raised to alter centre-section profile (*bottom*).

(a) Sailing along with H.M.S. *Protector*

(b) Old bird executes a near-vertical bank above a rough sea

(e) Turning with a wing-tip just clearing a rough sea

(f) Slow-speed flying. Rusty-pink 'collar' is just discernible

(i) Keeping a sharp lookout for food from 50 or 60 feet

(j) At top speed along the flank of a wave. Very rough sea

(c) Riding an updraught with constant small
adjustments of feet, wings and tail

(d) Diving to leeward before a moderate
gale. Wings partly 'reefed'

(g) High-speed turn into a wave trough
after downward dive

(h) Turning at 50 or 60 feet. Air-speed
much lower than in (e) and (g)

(k) Wings fully extended in a scimitar-like
curve

(l) Skimming low at very high speed. This
bird has given a rapid beat with right wing
primaries

Following H.M. Royal Yacht near the Falkland Islands. 6. Juvenile bird (*top*) and 7. adolescent female (*bottom*)

ing their eggs, but such calms in the waters they frequent are a rarity.

All agree that immense distances can be covered by albatrosses at a stretch, as has been proved beyond any doubt. An albatross caught, marked with paint and released, followed a ship for six successive days.* There is the remarkable case of the Wandering Albatross shot off the coast of Chile with a small vial hanging on a cord from its neck. In it was a message,† only twelve days old, from the whaler *Euphrates* in New Zealand waters. The shortest distance between the two ships was 3,150 miles. A bird ringed on Kerguelen Island was captured near Cape Horn, 6,083 miles away, by the French four-master *A. D. Bodes*. The *West Australian* of 21 August 1887 reported how a boy in the employment of a Mr V. E. Nesbit of Hay Street, Perth, found a dead albatross, whose body was still warm, lying on the beach at North Fremantle. There was a tin band round its neck on which a message had been punched: "13 NAUFRAGES SONT REFUGIES SUR LES ILES CROZET 4 AOUT 1887." The Crozet Islands are 3,500 miles from Perth. The Government was informed and a rescue party landed on the Crozets on September 30, where they found a further message from the shipwrecked men stating that their provisions were exhausted and that they were attempting to reach the neighbouring Possession Island—the last that was heard of the unfortunate thirteen.

Between 40° and 50° S. the globe is fourteen-fifteenths water and a bird could very easily work its way right round the world more than once during the months it spends at sea. Proven evidence is fragmentary, for the extensive ringing and recapture of birds which land only on remote islands, and range over an area ten times as large as the United States of America, are impossible. But such evidence as exists is conclusive and is borne out by the observations of many reliable witnesses. The distance through the air covered by a Wandering Albatross in

* Robert Cushman Murphy, *Oceanic Birds of South America*, Vol. I, 1936.
† The manuscript is in the Museum of Brown University, U.S.A.

the course of a year must amount to tens of thousands of miles.

They are great travellers, but the Southern Ocean is their home; those reported in the northern hemisphere have come there only through exceptional circumstances. In sailing-ship days the birds were often caught uninjured on a bait towed astern. Sometimes they were carried some distance and released again, which probably accounts for those reported far outside their usual range, even off the coasts of Britain. On 18 July 1894 a Mr J. A. Harvie-Brown, at sea 20 miles west of the Orkneys, saw a great bird which he was morally certain was an albatross.* Later that year an albatross, perhaps the same bird, was shot on the Faeroe Banks.† There are records, which seem well authenticated, of Wandering Albatrosses taken off Dieppe and Antwerp and, before Christmas 1909, a Mr Stubbs was astonished to see one hanging with the turkeys in the Leadenhall Market. As lately as 1952 a Blackbrowed Albatross, found entangled in the telegraph wires at Staveley, Derbyshire, caused a considerable stir. It was uninjured, and a benefactor had it taken by rail to Skegness, from which salubrious resort it disappeared over the North Sea.‡

As the day wore on two other albatrosses appeared, but the wind was dropping and the five birds were often far away. When the midday scraps were ditched they alighted to feed, remained on the water and eventually vanished astern. Their very long wings and high minimum flying speed are a serious embarrassment when taking off in light airs. If there is a swell they can remain airborne without too much effort, for great waves, moving steadily forward at 20 or 30 m.p.h., create up-draughts and eddies near the surface which the birds can make use of, flying with only an occasional wing-beat. In windless calms they usually rest on the water. In landing the great feet are splayed out, held well forward and used as water-brakes.

* *Annals Scottish Nat. Hist. Society*, No. 13, 1895.
† *Zoologist*, Vol. IV, Fourth Series.
‡ *British Birds*, Vol. XLVI, 1953.

It is rather an inelegant performance and once down the birds are obviously averse to rising again, because of the effort required. Heavy flapping and violent leg action are needed for 100 yards or so before attaining flying speed—a fussy and undignified procedure, very unlike their usual calm and dignified pose. The need for such large feet and their position so far aft on the bird's body is clearly demonstrated when they are rising off the water and there is little wind. Our forefathers, with their taste for the picturesque, used to say that albatrosses walked on the sea. Captain Weddell, in his account of his voyage towards the South Pole in the eighteen-twenties, stated that the noise of their tread could be heard at a considerable distance. Bullen * reports that the beating of their feet on the water is audible a long way off on a calm day.

November 28. We are about 600 miles S.S.W. of the Cape, on the edge of the Roaring Forties. As expected, yesterday's calm was the forerunner of a blow. During the day the strength of the wind gradually increased, and by mid-afternoon its force was 8 to 9 on the Beaufort Scale (48 to 56 m.p.h.). When I went on deck after breakfast the sky was a bright, pale blue and almost clear of clouds. Acres of ultramarine water marbled with foam stretched heaving to the horizon. Only three albatrosses were to be seen, but later we had no less than ten with us, sweeping joyously about at high speed. The Wandering Albatross is usually a solitary bird, each one searching his separate area of ocean, but they have learnt that a passing ship, stirring up the surface water and throwing out scraps, offers easier living. Patrolling birds spot a vessel from afar and gradually assemble astern, though only a few will remain with her through the night.

The great number of birds with us this afternoon gave me a splendid chance of observing the various plumage phases. Like some other sea-birds, albatrosses are dark-coloured when young, becoming progressively lighter as the feathers wear with

* Frank T. Bullen, *Creatures of the Sea*, 1904.

use and with each succeeding moult. Very young albatrosses just out of their natal down and wearing their first coat of feathers are a sombre black-brown all over, except for white across the forehead and on the sides of the face. (Plate 13.) Such birds are rarely seen outside the vicinity of the breeding grounds and it is reasonable to divide the ocean-going Wanderers into four groups—juvenile, adolescent, middle-aged and old.

More dark than white. Juvenile birds with white breasts, speckled with brown. The under sides of the wings are predominantly white except for the outer primaries. The upper surfaces are almost uniformly dark, with white feathers beginning to show on the back, which varies from dark to mottled. The head is white with a large dark crown-patch and a wide dark collar round the neck. Tail dark above and below (Plate 6).

Half-white, half-dark. These adolescent birds are two to three years old and have replaced many more of their dark feathers with white ones. The belly and the under sides of the wings are now almost entirely white, except for the outer primaries and a few dark flecks along the sides of the body and around the neck. The back is white, speckled with darker feathers, and white has spread in a V to the centre of the upper wing surfaces, where there are white specks amongst the outer secondaries. Rump and tail are white, but the tail is still edged with black. The dark crown-patch is smaller; in young males it may be entirely absent.

More white than dark. These are middle-aged birds. They are pure white below, except for a narrow border on the trailing edge of the wings (which may never quite disappear) and the black outer primaries. Their backs are almost pure white, with a few dark flecks on the shoulders. The general effect of the upper wing surfaces is a white inner half, speckled with black; outer secondaries and primaries are dark. A few dark flecks are all that remains of the dark tail-bar, and the crown-patch has vanished from all except the females, who never lose it entirely —an infallible guide to sex.

Predominantly white. Old birds, in the full magnificence of their snowy plumage. It used to be thought that this was a separate species (*Diomedea chionoptera*),* but Matthews and others have proved that it is only a separate, and final, colour phase. The tail is now white above and below. The wings, except for the primaries and tips of the outer secondaries, which are jet black, and perhaps the narrow wing-edge already referred to (Plate 2), are pure white all over. Females retain a small dark crown-patch. The general effect is of a great snow-white bird, the black which remains accentuating the dazzling purity of the rest of its plumage.

November 29. Still blowing as hard as ever and, by the glass, worse is to come. The sea had risen during the night and when dawn came slowly we saw, under an overcast sky, waves 300 or 400 yards from crest to crest with troughs 30 or 35 feet deep. The deck was plunging up and down and lurching from side to side. No flying today! We are too far from home and dare not risk damage to our precious machines.

I fought my way into a corner where there was some shelter from the full force of the blast and wedged myself against the motion of the ship, which was already considerable. There was a lot of noise from the wind buffeting past and from the wild waves rearing up and falling away. The sea was tremendous—an awe-inspiring sight even from the deck of a great ship several hundred times as large as the tiny vessels in which the early navigators first explored these waters. Small wonder that Forster wrote in 1773 that the gale "tossed our poor ship strangely to and from." It was wild but splendid weather. Our man-made machines were storm-bound, but the albatrosses were enjoying themselves—swooping round at high speed, banking, soaring, diving to within an inch or two of the sea; perfectly at home in their boisterous element and moving, as it seemed, in any direction they wished.

I counted eight in company, juvenile, adolescent and middle-

* *Chion* = snow; *pteron* = feather or wing; hence *chionoptera*.

aged birds and one white oldster—the same old male, as I believed, who has been with us all along. On the course we were following the wind-speed over the deck was between 50 and 60 m.p.h. Around the ship were eddies and up-draughts which, had we been able to see them, would have looked like the water round a rock in a torrent. The great birds seemed to know just where to find the air currents they needed. Some preferred to maintain their usual elliptical track, but others would hang, poised a few feet off, riding the turbulent wind on outstretched wings. At this close range the constant small movements of wings, feet and tail by which the bird kept its trim and retained its exact flying speed were noticeable, but it was an easy, unhurried performance.

As I stood there the old white male took up a position abreast and a little above me and gave me a chance to examine him in detail as he floated along a few feet off, gravely staring back at me from one large, round, dark-brown eye.

The great hooked beak, carried at a downward slope, is six or eight inches long (see drawing on page 93). Beak colour varies according to the season from pink to buff. This bird's beak was flesh-pink shading off to near-white at the tip. The eye is so dark a brown that from a distance it looks black. The eyelids are greenish white, though birds with bright pink eyelids have been reported, and Elliott, who resided on Tristan da Cunha from January 1950 to October 1952 states that the Wanderers which nest in this area have bright blue eyelids.* Sight, as in most birds, must be extremely keen. Even today a small scrap dancing in the raging welter of the wake would instantly be noted and swooped upon. The neck is comparatively short. One middle-aged bird had a narrow collar of rusty pink. This pink staining has frequently been noted and may appear as a ring or simply as a patch on one or both sides of the head. Some say it denotes breeding birds, but nesting birds may or may not carry it, though Elliott reports that only very immature birds on

* H. F. I. Elliott, "A Contribution to the Ornithology of the Tristan da Cunha Group," *Ibis*, Vol. 99, No. 4, 1957.

Gough Island are without this beautiful rose-pink flush, which can be seen in the field at a considerable distance.

The body is beautifully streamlined, with the legs set very far back, carried pointing dead astern and blending with the smooth run aft. The feet, darker coloured than the beak (they also vary in colour with the seasons from pink to light grey), are very large, extending several inches beyond the tail in flight and are used as a supplementary control surface. The wings, like those of a modern high-performance sailplane, are very narrow—9 inches maximum width for a bird with a spread of over 10 feet. There is the normal number of primary feathers (ten) on the outer wing-bone, but the intermediate and inner bones are exceptionally long to accommodate no less than forty secondary feathers (most birds have six to twelve) and well-developed tertiaries. The wings are beautifully formed for high-speed gliding and maximum lift, with a pronounced camber. In level flight they are often held in a downward-sweeping arc, with the tips lower than the body (see Plate 4A). In plan their shape varies from a flat, scimitar-like curve, when soaring or banking, to a wide W, which is most pronounced in the rapid downward dive. By adjusting the spread of its wings in this way the bird controls their lift. When the wind is very high they can, as it were, reef their wings—as old sailormen used graphically to express it.

It was noticeable that individual birds would often fly on exactly the same track relative to the ship, each one selecting a chosen course and keeping to it religiously—soaring up against the wind to 50 or 60 feet, flying level for a while and then diving down-wind at very high speed. When just above the water a steeply banked turn brought the bird into a trough between the waves with its wing-tip only a few inches clear of the very rough sea.

The birds alighted to feed far more frequently than in calm weather, lifting their wings high above the body, part-folding them and touching down as lightly as a feather. Usually the wings would be held up clear of the water and kept partly

8. South Georgia. The waddling gait

9. Old cock standing beside young hen

10. Old cock, brooding. Bay of Isles, South Georgia

11. Middle-aged hen and newly-hatched chick

spread whilst the bird seized whatever it was after. In the language of a bygone age, the albatross "is as careful of wetting the soft under-feathers of his wings as a lady is of protecting the hem of her petticoat against the mud of the kennel."* To take off, they faced the wind, paddled to a crest, spread their wings and were wafted into the air without any apparent effort. They are said sometimes to swoop on their food without actually alighting, but all I observed behaved as reported by the Earl and the Doctor who "never yet saw an albatross which did not sit down, soberly and calmly, to his dinner." * Green † states categorically that an albatross cannot strike from the air, must settle to feed and will only do so if sure of the nature of its prey.

The gale increased in strength during the day. Wave-tops, torn by the wind and hurled to leeward, filled the air with spindrift. By evening the storm was at its height and the albatrosses had gradually disappeared. It has frequently been noted that the number of birds in sight falls off heavily under such conditions, though one or two may remain if the ship is running before the gale. As soon as the storm is past they return remarkably quickly. Where have they been? There is no shelter within hundreds of miles and they certainly do not, as was once believed, "soar into the upper regions of the atmosphere, in which they . . . enjoy a calm, while the fury of the blast is expending itself below." ‡ The French scientist Idrac, whose work will be referred to in detail in a later chapter, has calculated that in very high winds the albatross cannot maintain its position and must be swept away to leeward of a ship steaming into or across the gale. Before this point is reached, and the birds vanish from view, they begin to flap their wings to a considerable extent, though making the maximum use of eddies and rising air currents on the flanks of the swell to obtain lift, crossing quickly over the "cols" between waves to another trough and avoiding the crests where the wind is highest and the air

* Lord Pembroke and Dr E. H. Kingsley, *South Sea Bubbles*, 1873.
† *Ocean Birds*.
‡ Thomas Nuttall, A.M., F.L.S., *The Water Birds*, 1834.

C

most heavily charged with spray. As spindrift fills the troughs, increasing the resistance of the air, gliding flight becomes virtually impossible even at the lowest levels sheltered from the full force of the wind. The birds are forced to make more and more use of their wings, until they reach the limit of muscular endurance. Perhaps they settle and ride it out, keeping as far as possible in the comparative shelter of the troughs. It is one of the gaps in our knowledge which still remains unfilled.

When the last of the birds had disappeared I went rather sadly below. Staunch modern vessels give us comfort and security, but the pitting of seamanship against the storm has gone. We are left to imagine what it was like in the days of sail. Under conditions like these, clippers, running their Easting down before the gale, would cover between 300 and 400 miles in twenty-four hours—a better day's run than many a steamship. But it was only the skill of the men at the wheel which averted constantly menacing disaster, for the ship must on no account broach to across the path of the great waves which, travelling at twice her speed, towered above the counter. The slightest error could throw her on her beam ends, perhaps to become a total loss. As the clipper ships surged forward, day after day, along these stormy latitudes an albatross would often be with them,

level with the mizenmast head and a little to windward, is found [our] snowy companion, apparently motionless except for an almost imperceptible bending of the wings and tail, his beautiful snowy head with its dark, solemn eyes turning gravely from side to side in keenest watchfulness.*

November 30. The wind dropped during the night, though the sea was still huge—immense blue rollers rushing eastward under the bright sky. Four of the younger albatrosses joined us at intervals during the day, but our old friend failed to reappear. Perhaps he is off to the place where he was hatched and where he probably returns to breed. The nearest nesting ground from

* *Creatures of the Sea.*

our position (42° S. and 15° E.) would be in the Crozet Islands, nearly 2,000 miles away. Breeding birds begin to assemble in these remote and stormy spots in late November and early December, coming in from their lonely life over the open ocean to spend a few months with their mates and in close proximity with others of their kind. The old males are the first to arrive at these islands, which are spread round the globe between thirty-seven and fifty-five degrees south latitude—Kerguelen, Macquarie, Campbell, Auckland, Antipodes, South Georgia, Tristan da Cunha, Gough, Marion, Prince Edward and the Crozets. Some are uninhabited; all are lonely and inaccessible.

2. *Egg to Adolescence*

THE origin of every bird can be traced back to the flying rep-
tiles of prehistoric times. Through countless ages the friction
of the struggle for existence has moulded and adapted various
bird-forms to meet the conditions of survival. Thirty or forty
million years ago the albatrosses evolved to something very like
their present form. Traces of an early albatross have been
found in rocks dating from the Miocene Epoch (10 to 30 million B.C.). The Procellariiformes or Tubinares (tube-noses)—
the great petrel tribe of which the albatrosses are a sub-family—
belong to an ancient order which has few other survivors. There
are some fourteen sub-species of albatrosses, of which two, three
or four (science still differs on their exact classification) are the
"great" albatrosses. By common consent the greatest of them
all is the Wandering Albatross. Sailors have called it by a
variety of names—Goney, Cape Sheep, Chocolate Albatross,
Man-of-War Bird, Toroa. It features in the catalogue of birds
of the British Museum as *Diomedea exulans*.

In the middle of the eighteenth century Linnaeus decided to
avoid the confusion of local nomenclature by giving universal
names to plants, birds and beasts. In dealing with the Wander-

ing Albatross he seems to have been guided by two fables. There had long been a legend that the souls of dead sea-captains thought by their crews to have had the best of it in their life-times in snug quarters in the poop, were condemned after death to wander eternally above the cold and stormy southern seas. John Reinold Forster, naturalist with Captain Cook on his second great voyage (1772–75), remarks on this belief. Linnaeus classified the Wandering Albatross in 1766, so the fable was evidently current at that time. *"Diomedea"* comes from Diomedes, a Thracian who, after the Trojan wars, went to Italy, ran foul of a magician and had his companions turned into birds resembling swans. *Exulans* (more properly *exsulsans*) was an equally apposite choice. It means being an exile, a wanderer with no fixed abode. *Diomedea exulans!* A noble-sounding name for the noblest of birds.

Early books on natural history contain brief, not always accurate, references to the albatross. Eleazar Albin, in *A Natural History of Birds*, published in 1738, includes a plate of a Wandering Albatross over the title Man-of-War Bird, but remarks that it is "also called the Albitross." In 1747 George Edwards published in London another *Natural History of Birds*, in Part II of which he dealt with the rarer varieties, "Most of which have not been figured or described, and others very little known, from obscure or too brief Descriptions without Figures, or from Figures very ill designed." Edwards pointed out that Albin had been in error in confounding the albatross with the man-of-war bird—"for on examining voyagers on that head I find they make the Man-of-War Bird a much smaller bird; and they who have mentioned the Albatross make it of the first magnitude of water-fowl; so that I can by no means agree they are the same birds." Pennant's *Arctic Zoology* (1785) refers sometimes accurately to the albatrosses which "wander over all parts of the Antarctic Seas" and sometimes confuses them with other birds "watching the motions of the Flying Fish, which they catch when these miserable beings spring out of their element to shun the jaws of Coryphenes." Latham's *General*

Synopsis of Birds, published the same year, contains an accurate description of *Diomedea exulans*—"in great plenty in the neighbourhood of the Cape of Good Hope, as all voyagers can testify; and . . . from thence in every temperate southern latitude as far towards the Pole as has yet been explored." Latham gives particulars of their nests and eggs, but concludes with some strange remarks how "as soon as the young are able to remove from the nest, the Penguins take possession and hatch their young in turn."

It was not until the late eighteenth century that natural history, which had been the occasional study of a few, became a more popular science. Fortunately this change took place in the great age of sail, when many ships sought out the "albatross latitudes" to take advantage of the prevailing westerly winds in the Roaring Forties (40–50° S.). Such ships spent weeks in the zone where albatrosses are most abundant, and the notes of many observers provide valuable information about the behaviour of the birds when at sea.

Early references to the albatross ashore on its nesting sites are usually confined to the palatability or otherwise of the bird, its eggs and its young. In the eighteenth and early nineteenth centuries mariners were sometimes cast away on the remote islands where the Wandering Albatross lands to breed, but few displayed much interest in the bird, except as something for the table. One or two made notes which are of value, notably Mr Richard Harris, R.N., of His Majesty's ship *Adventure* in 1832.

The era of accurate information might be said to begin with the sending out of well-equipped scientific expeditions at the beginning of the present century such as the *Discovery* (1901–4 and 1925–27) the *Quest* (1921–22), and to the journeyings of such highly qualified observers as Robert Cushman Murphy (1936), Niall Rankin (1951) and L. E. Richdale (1952). It is to the writings of these scientists and of those who compiled the ornithological sections of the expeditions reports—notably G. H. Wilkins of the *Quest*, L. Harrison Matthews of the *Discovery*— that we owe the picture of the life-cycle of the Wandering Alba-

tross which can now be drawn. There are still gaps to be filled,
but it is fairly complete, particularly when dealing with the bird
ashore.

Imagine a remote island set down in the stormiest and loneliest seas in the world. Even in summer the weather is usually
bad. The wind nearly always seems to be blowing, often at gale
force. Rare fine spells are sandwiched between many days of
rain, sleet or even snow. It is a bleak, treeless place, the vegeta-
tion below the rocks and ice of the higher ground consisting of
coarse tussock grass, grey-green in colour and sometimes three
or four feet high. Until 200 years ago no man ever penetrated
these high southern latitudes and even today there are few
traces of his existence, except around the scattered settlements
of whalers and sealers. But the island is teeming with life; with
birds and beasts which get their living from the surrounding
seas—as rich in food as any in the world. A few of these creatures are permanently shore-based, but the majority are pelagic,
landing only to breed and raise their young. Then they throng
the coastal waters and the shore in their thousands and even
spread inland from the sea. They range from lumbering sea-
elephants weighing several tons to tiny Wilson's petrels. The
beaches are alive with the slumbering forms of various kinds of
seal. Great flocks of birds wheel through the air and bob upon
the water, and the hillsides are dotted with the rookeries of
penguins, albatrosses and other fowl.

Somewhere not far from the coast in a position exposed to the
prevailing wind and probably on a slight eminence will be found
the nests of the Wandering Albatrosses. The birds, so solitary
at sea, collect in quite large numbers when ashore, leading a
semi-communal life though never acting together as a flock.

For a bird with so high a minimum flying speed, whose legs
are primarily designed to help it alight on, or rise from the sea,
the choice of a breeding site is governed by the hazards of landing and taking off. On shore albatrosses are clumsy birds.
Unlike some of the tube-noses they can at least stand upright,

but they walk laboriously with a waddling gait and find it difficult to run fast enough to get airborne unless helped by the
wind or falling ground. Landing is a precarious business frequently attended with disaster—the bird coming down heavily,
falling forward on to its chest or even turning a somersault. To
minimise these risks albatrosses build their nests on a comparatively flat "airfield" in an exposed position near a slope or cliff
from which they can launch themselves into the air. Shelter
and warmth are not considered and albatrosses will be found
happily brooding and rearing their young under conditions
which would kill a man from exposure in a very short time, but
the birds remain warm, dry and seemingly quite comfortable
inside the thick covering of feathers which deflects the wet and
insulates them most effectively from the low average temperature.

Geography has scattered the breeding sites of the Wandering
Albatross unevenly in, or very near the edges of, the sub-
Antarctic zone. There are gaps of nearly 90 degrees of
longitude between Kerguelen and Macquarie Islands and no
less than 145 degrees between the Antipodes Islands and South
Georgia. The northernmost site is in the Tristan da Cunha
group (37° S.) and the southernmost in South Georgia (54° 30'
S.). There is no record of *Diomedea exulans* nesting on St
Paul's or Bouvet Islands. Bouvet, though in much the same
latitude as South Georgia, is further outside the sub-Antarctic
zone, rises precipitously to nearly 3,000 feet above sea level and
is almost entirely covered with an ice-cap. St Paul's, like
Tristan da Cunha, is in the high thirties of south latitude, but
lies well within the sub-Tropical zone of warmer surface water,
which takes a southward sweep in these longitudes. The coasts
and islands of southern South America, though located
inside the prescribed zone, are used by the Royal (*Diomedea
epomophora*) but not by the Wandering Albatross, though both
species share the amenities, such as they are, of Campbell
Island, south of New Zealand. Wanderers are seen around the
South Sandwich group and Heard Island, but do not breed

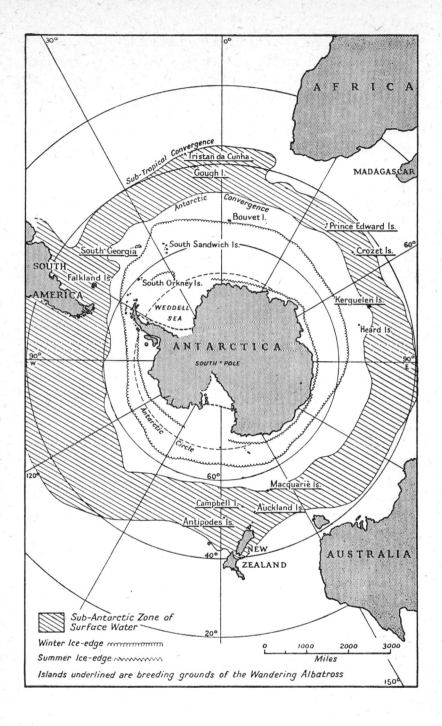

30°   0°

AFRICA

MADAGASCAR

Sub-Tropical Convergence

Tristan da Cunha

Gough I.

Antarctic Convergence

Bouvet I.

Prince Edward Is.

South Georgia

South Sandwich Is.

Crozet Is.

60°

SOUTH

Falkland Is.

South Orkney Is.

AMERICA

WEDDELL SEA

Kerguelen Is.

Heard Is.

90° W

ANTARCTICA

SOUTH POLE

90° E

Antarctic

Circle

120°

60°

Macquarie Is.

Campbell I.

Auckland Is.

Antipodes Is.

40°

NEW ZEALAND

AUSTRALIA

20°

Sub-Antarctic Zone of Surface Water

Winter Ice-edge

Summer Ice-edge

0   1000   2000   3000

Miles

Islands underlined are breeding grounds of the Wandering Albatross

150°

there. Both places belong definitely to the Antarctic zone and are much closer to the ice-edge than any known nesting site. There is evidently a limit to the rigours which even these well-insulated birds are prepared to endure.

Most of our information about the nesting habits of *Diomedea exulans* comes from South Georgia, where the birds have probably bred for thousands of years. Sparrman, who was with Captain Cook when the island was discovered in 1775, describes how on New Year's day, "we rowed with the Captain . . . to a place where thousands of *pelicans* had built their nests." Sparrman's error points to the origin of the word albatross—derived from *alcatraz*, which is the Portuguese for pelican.

Nests are usually spaced fairly regularly 20 to 50 yards apart, and from the sea the great white birds show up very clearly, dotting a hillside like geese on a common. The size of some colonies may be very large. Four men from the *Quest* (Shackleton–Rowatt Expedition) collected 3,500 albatross eggs of various sorts, in three days at the northern end of South Georgia in 1923. Mankind has found both eggs and young to be good eating. On the other hand, the whaling industry has supplied the birds with large quantities of easily won food and some sort of a balance seems to have been established.

The nest is shaped like a miniature volcano, with a shallow bowl hollowed out at the top in which the single egg is laid. The bottom of these circular, conical nests always measures about three feet across, but the height varies between one and three feet, and is designed to keep the top above the level of winter snows, which do not lie very deep in such exposed positions. Green * remarked that a deserted nest makes a remarkably convenient seat!

Both birds assist in building these often considerable structures, but the male does most of the work. They first scrape out a circular trench with their beaks, piling the soil and green matter from it in the centre. Soil, moss and tussock grass are then collected, added to the heap and trampled down into a

* *Ocean Birds.*

solid mass resembling peat. As the nesting sites are usually located on a tussock-covered hillside material is readily available. Wandering Albatrosses are believed to return year after year to the same breeding site, and old nests are often repaired and used again. Both birds will usually be seen around the nest whilst it is being built or repaired, but a few days before the egg is laid the male may go off to sea for a while, leaving the female undisturbed. Sitting birds continue to perfect their nests, adding new material and smoothing the surface with their beaks.

There is a slight variation in the date when the first eggs are laid in the various islands from the last days of November (Campbell Island), to December 26 (Gough Island). In South Georgia, where the sites have been most continuously observed, laying begins on December 13 but most birds lay in the last week of that month. By early January (midsummer) eggs are everywhere plentiful.

The single egg varies in shape and appearance, but is usually somewhat elongated with a coarse white shell speckled with red spots, which are more numerous at the larger end. On South Georgia, eggs weigh about 15 ounces and hold three-quarters of a pint of liquid (six hen's eggs). The average size of the Gough Island egg is smaller, and it is now commonly agreed that the Wandering Albatrosses which breed there and in the Tristan da Cunha area are a sub-species of *Diomedea exulans*, slightly smaller than the birds nesting further south. The eggs are excellent eating, the yolks a good golden yellow and the whites setting when cooked, and many are taken by whalers and sealers. Opinions differ as to whether a robbed female will always lay again that season, but the numbers of albatrosses do not seem to be dwindling very seriously, though accurate records are lacking. Rankin (1951) estimated the Wandering Albatross population of South Georgia as being in the region of 6,000 birds in 1946–47, but I know of no previous or subsequent attempt at a census.

Brooding is a long business, it is nine or ten weeks—probably 72 days—before the chick appears. Male and female take turns on the nest and are rarely seen together after the egg is laid.

There is a wide variation in, and some difference of opinion about, the length of the brooding spells; no one has yet spent more than two months keeping a continuous watch on the bleak and windswept nesting sites. G. H. Wilkins (of the *Quest*) camped ashore on South Georgia from 16 December 1921 to 1 January 1922. Birds began to lay on December 21 and brooding birds were relieved at intervals of four to twenty-four hours. Other observers (Matthews, Murphy and Rankin) are convinced that a brooding bird may remain much longer than this on the nest, working a cycle of three to eleven days duration if the food supply necessitates long journeys by the "non-duty" bird. The brooding bird is not fed by its mate, loses weight and condition and becomes stained and dirty after sitting for long periods on the nest—contrasting strongly with the plump and glossy partner who eventually takes its place.

Eggs and newly-hatched young are guarded from the depredations of the fierce and piratical Arctic Skuas which are always on the look-out for an easy meal, but albatrosses on their nests show neither fear nor resentment of man. If approached they will snap their great bills once or twice as a warning that liberties are not permitted. Migot * has described how the bird looking magnificent on its high nest, will not move away, but gazes at the visitor with a lovely, clear eye and hardly seems at all nervous. As with all animals, sudden movements must be avoided, but the birds are so fearless and tame that they can be stroked and even lifted gently from the nest to examine the egg, though a firm grasp on the fearsome bill is a wise precaution. Matthews (1929) confirms these observations.

Captain Wilkinson of H.M.S. *Protector*, who visited the breeding site on the Bay of Isles, South Georgia, in January and March 1957, found the birds sitting patiently and benignly on their nests; not at all worried by his close approach, and only slightly put out if levered gently upwards to reveal the egg—so muffled amongst the thick breast-feathers that the bulge of its shape was visible long before the shell came to light. Murphy

* André Migot, *The Lonely South*, 1956.

(1948), with his usual felicity of phrase, tells how he crouched close beside the nest of a sitting bird and looked into its large, brown, expressive eye, and how, after a few moments, the bird laid its head on the soft pillow of its back. "Like a great goose," said the Danes of the *Galathea* Expedition (1950–52), "but a charming goose."

In spite of what has been reported in an earlier chapter it is fair to conclude that the Wandering Albatross is devoid of aggressiveness. It has no natural enemies but the skua, which will not tackle a grown bird, and man is too infrequent a visitor to be regarded with suspicion. The albatross only attacks what it mistakes for its usual food. It never feeds on land. At sea, like the bears in some of America's National Parks, it can be dangerous without evil intent. (The remark of the American park warden is apposite. Asked by a lady why she must not feed the bear, he replied, "You see, Ma'am, the crittur don't rightly know where the bun stops and your arm begins.")

Fearlessness is not confined to the breeding period. Captain Dixon described how, when his ship was becalmed, a swimming albatross approached the boat they had lowered. "We could have patted his head—if his head had been muzzled. We held out a piece of fat on a stick. He took it. We left a piece on the gunwhale of the boat. He took that." *

Early in March (corresponding to September in our latitude) the eggs begin to chip, but it is four or five days † before the chicks are clear of the shell, clean and dry. Newly hatched youngsters weigh 11 to 14 ounces and are covered all over with silky, pure white down. The beak, which is hooked at this stage, and the feet are yellow, and the bright eyes so dark a brown as to appear almost black. One of the old birds continues to brood and guard the chick, which would soon fall a victim to a skua if left unattended. The sitting birds hiss, half-rising from their

---

* Captain C. C. Dixon, "Some Observations on the Albatrosses and Other Birds of the Southern Ocean," *Trans. Roy. Canadian Institute*, Vol. XIX, 1933.
† Rankin.

nests if the skuas pass too close overhead, but these gentry are very quick and agile, both in the air and on the ground, and an albatross wandering too far from the nest will see its chick snatched whilst it is still waddling furiously back into range. Newly hatched young, like the egg, are brooded more or less encased in the sack of feathers at the bottom of the tummy of the sitting bird.*

Growth is very rapid. From an average hatching weight of 12½ ounces chicks have increased to 1 pound 4 ounces in a week, 2 pounds 4 ounces in ten days and 4 pounds 6 ounces in three weeks, when they are as big as barn-yard fowls. The average weight of chicks only one month old at a South Georgia colony was over 6½ pounds †—almost ten times the hatching weight. These chicks had put on nearly 3½ ounces a day!

The parents continue to take it in turns to guard and feed the young, which chirp importunately when hungry. When the foraging bird returns from sea the chick places its bill inside and across that of its parent to take the regurgitated food which consists first of fish and later fish and cuttlefish. After about a month both parents may be absent at sea together as the skuas have ceased to molest the young.

The youngsters are now developing the second (mesotyle) coat of luxuriant down which keeps them warm in the absence of the brooding bird. This down is a buffish-grey and very dense. The autumn is now well advanced—it would be November in our latitudes. Winter is not far away and frequent storms sweep over the exposed nesting sites, but the young albatross, well insulated from the cold, seems quite indifferent to the weather.

In May the young are still being fed, but less frequently, the parents remaining only for a few minutes, sitting beside the nest just long enough to pass the regurgitated food which the youngster, after nibbling their throat-feathers and making a gobbling cry, swallows with avidity. Quite large fish and cuttlefish will be brought to them at this stage.

* Wilkinson.
† A number of birds weighed by Rankin averaged 105 ounces.

The young bird is more aggressive than its parents. If approached by man it sits back in the nest and swivels rapidly round so as always to face the intruder, whom it warns to keep his distance by rapid snapping of the bill and a gobbling sound rather like a turkey. If the visitor persists, the youngster will discharge its stomach contents, mixed with a very evil-smelling oil, which has a curious, musky odour, very clinging and persistent if it finds its way on to your clothes.

All the tube-nose family, including the albatrosses and the petrels, have supplies of this stomach oil, yellow or pink in colour and chemically somewhat similar to the oil found in the head of the sperm whale. It is a gland secretion and not the undigested residue of their food, and can be discharged through the beak or through the prominent nostrils which are so distinctive a feature of the tribe. Even today the exact function of this oil is not known. It is certainly used as a weapon of defence, particularly by the petrels, which can fire it over a fair distance and with considerable accuracy. It may be a supplemental food for the young and seems to pass when the chicks are feeding, particularly in the early stage of growth. It is rich in vitamin A, and contains vitamin D, but the comparatively low protein content indicates that this is not its main use, though the oil is easily digested and is used by the Maoris of New Zealand in preparing food. It has been suggested that these true ocean-going birds use it to calm the waters in their immediate vicinity when riding out a gale—not as absurd as it may sound, as anyone who has tried the effect of even a small quantity of oil on a turbulent sea will testify. Oil could be discharged from the nostrils along the distinctive grooves in the beak when preening. Feather-dressing is of the utmost importance to creatures which spend so much time in the air. The oil contains alcohol and remains fluid at low temperatures and would easily be transferred from beak to feathers (Murphy). Finally it has been suggested by Matthews * that the oil is the source of the fledgling's water supply, the majority of the young tube-noses being fed only once

* L. Harrison Matthews, *The Origin of Stomach Oil in Petrels*, 1949.

daily after the first few weeks and later abandoned by their
parents for several months before they themselves go off to sea.
It is possible that all the theories advanced are partly true; they
are not mutually exclusive.

We now come to a point in the life-story of the young albatross about which very little is certainly known. The Antarctic
winter is closing down. Days are short, storms more frequent
than ever and it is becoming more and more difficult to observe
the birds at their nesting sites. In May the young are sitting as
usual on their nests and are still being fed at intervals of 24 hours
or longer. The youngsters are now as big as their parents and
very fat, covered with down and of course cannot fly. There are
no dependable records covering the next two months, though
Richard Harris,* who spent the winter months on Kerguelen
in 1833, stated that all the old birds had left the island in June.

South Georgia is probably under snow in August, not lying
thickly in such exposed places, but level with the tops of the
nests. Matthews,† visiting a site during this month, describes
how each nest had "a young albatross the size of a small sheep
sitting on it, sitting all alone and waiting; clad in a thick coat of
buffish woolly down." At this age the fat young Goneys are
said to make very good eating.

In October and November the sites are again regularly
under observation; the youngsters are there, but no old birds
will at first be seen. Some time in the winter, probably in June,
the young birds have been left to their own resources, to live on
their fat and to wait for the time when they have grown their
first coat of feathers and learnt to fly. All we know for certain is
that young Wandering Albatrosses remain in their nests for
eight or nine months after they are hatched, that the old birds
seem to vanish in May or June and that the young are still
there when the breeding birds come ashore again in November
and December.

* F. W. Hutton, "Notes on some of the Birds inhabiting the Southern
Ocean." *Ibis.* New Series, Vol. I, 1865.
† L. Harrison Matthews, *Wandering Albatross,* 1951.

Young Goneys. 12.
With feathers growing
underneath the down
(*top*) and 13. in the
black-brown dress
(*bottom*)

Bigger than they look over the sea. 14. On Kerguelen (*top*) and 15. South Georgia (*bottom*)

It is an unsolved mystery. *Facts* about the all-important period from May to November—the Antarctic winter and spring—are lacking. We have no absolute proof of what occurs—only a strong supposition which has been supported in recent years by such authorities as Matthews (1929), Murphy (1936) and Rankin (1951). By June the frame of the young bird is fully grown. Rankin has calculated that if youngsters continue to maintain the same rate of weight-increase they will be considerably heavier than the old birds when left to their own resources, with adequate supplies of blubber on which to live until they can fly and forage for themselves. Young birds found on and around the nests at the end of November and early December are not yet feeding themselves and do not make a serious effort to do so until driven off by the returning breeding birds. They are in good condition, but the stomachs of those examined have been found to be quite empty. A number of animals and birds can support life for long periods without food, a characteristic of several inhabitants of the Antarctic which acquire great layers of fat when well fed. The great sea-elephant bulls of South Georgia—beasts weighing three tons—go through much of the breeding season, when they are mating and fighting at frequent intervals, without eating. The fulmar, a member of the tube-nose family which has been closely and scientifically observed, goes for several weeks without food when the young birds are abandoned by their parents.* Murphy says that the metabolic process of the young albatrosses, sitting out the rigours of the Antarctic winter on their nests, must be very slow, and describes their conditions as "the nearest approach to hibernation found in the bird world." †

On the other hand, Richdale believes that the old birds continue to feed their young, though at infrequent intervals which may extend to several days. He states categorically that feeding by the parents continues until the young can fly.‡ It is possible, in the solitudes where they breed, with short winter days and

* James Fisher, *The Fulmar*, 1952.   † *Oceanic Birds*, Vol. I.
    ‡ L. E. Richdale, *Post-Egg Period in Albatrosses*, 1952.
D

bad weather making continuous observations so difficult that the occasional return of the parents has not been noted—possible, but not very probable, for many observers have noted the absence of older birds from June to November.

However, Richdale is an authority whose views cannot be lightly discounted. He has had unique opportunities for observing the behaviour of another of the "great" albatrosses—*Diomedea epomophora*, the Royal Albatross. These birds have a nesting site at Tairoroa Head, New Zealand, which Richdale has had under observation for no less than 17 years, visiting the place at such close intervals as to be perfectly sure of his facts. The Royal Albatross is, of course, a separate and distinct species from *Diomedea exulans*, but its habits and behaviour *may* throw light on those of the other bird. Royals continue to feed their young from hatching to sea-going—an average period of seven to eight months (236 days). The young are guarded for 40 days, fed every other day for the next two months, and thereafter at increasing intervals; but *fed* two days before they go to sea. Richdale believes that the same behaviour can be expected in Wanderers and quotes Turbott (1951) as having seen *D. exulans* being fed at their nesting sites on Antipodes Island within four to six weeks of flying. Exactly what happens between May and October remains a mystery, but I believe, with Matthews, Murphy and Rankin, that the young are abandoned for several months. As Murphy expresses it, "data on the life of young albatrosses are drawn from many scattered sources . . . but they piece together to form the only hypothesis consistent with the known facts." *

When spring is at last on the way, the breeding sites of *D. exulans* on the remoter islands are more frequently visited and accurate information about what is going on is available. Gould † records that young Wandering Albatrosses are on their nests in October. Hutton ‡ says that deserted young ones observed in October 1832 on Prince Edward Island by Mr

* *Oceanic Birds*, Vol. I.   † *Birds of Australia.*
‡ "Notes on birds inhabiting the Southern Ocean."

Richard Harris, R.N., of Her Majesty's Ship *Adventure* were in good condition and very lively, frequently being noticed off their nests exercising their wings. Harris does not agree with the belief current at that time that these young birds go to the sea at night to feed. He never saw one on the wing until the old ones returned, although he spent many weeks ashore after his ship was wrecked, whilst a boat was being constructed in which his party eventually reached Australia.

All through the winter the first coat of feathers has been growing underneath the second coat of down. By October the young birds are feathered all over, though considerable tufts of down may still be adhering to the tips of the feathers, particularly on the flanks and wing scapulars, and there is matted down, like sheep's wool, on their bellies. Except for the white sides of the face and a white bridge across the nose like a pair of spectacles, the feathers are black-brown—a chocolate colour. The beak is a whitish yellow, the legs and feet light grey. A young albatross is a sombre bird, very different from the splendid creature it will eventually become.

In November the young are getting ready to fly. Their great wings are still weak, but they are strengthening them by spreading and flapping them as they waddle around the nesting sites. Murphy (1948) has described the next stage—how birds would stand facing the wind, spreading their long, weak wings to the full extent, beat about in rather a wobbly manner for a few minutes and finally spring off the ground and remain airborne for a few seconds. Migot (1956) observed on Kerguelen that the young birds took a month practising to fly, and it is corroborated by Murphy and Wilkins that the bird which will eventually become such a master of the air is a slow learner. Wilkins (1923) watched young birds laboriously waddling up a hillside taking frequent rests on the way and then, after a prolonged rest, run a few steps downhill and launch themselves into the air for a short flight, followed by a heavy landing which probably sent them tail over beak. Getting up, with an expression of pained surprise, they would repeat the process, always

toiling further up the hill if failing to get properly airborne.

From December to January both old and young birds use
the sites and young birds are seen flying over the sea near the
land, though "obviously making heavy weather of it." * Matthews noted on one visit ashore in November that "not one
young bird was to be seen on the site," though as late as March,
when the new season's eggs were hatching out, "a few of last
season's young were sitting about in their black-brown plumage." The scientific results of the voyage of the *Challenger* in
1873–76 report on the other hand that no young were seen at
Kerguelen in January, to the great disappointment of the
whalers, who had been looking forward to a succulent dish.
Hutton (1865), who made a close study of the birds of the
Southern Ocean during seven voyages, believes that the young
birds do not go far from land until they accompany their parents
to the open ocean later in the year, though Murphy states that
he has taken a number of black-brown birds in their first chocolate plumage as much as 1,000 miles from land.

We must again be guided by the weight of the available evidence. Young birds begin to fly in November, when the old
birds return, remaining in the vicinity of the nests until January.
From January to June they gradually extend their range over
the open sea. Stragglers remain on the sites, but leave with the
the last of the breeding birds. The fully fledged youngsters now
begin the purely pelagic existence which they will follow for
several years. Some of them may not see land again until the
return to the place where they were hatched to breed. Four,
five, six or even seven years may elapse before this happens.
Not for nothing has the bird been named the Wandering
Albatross.

* Murphy.

3. *Fable*

God save thee, ancient Mariner,
From the fiends, that plague thee thus!—
Why look'st thou so?—"With my crossbow
I shot the Albatross."

Samuel Taylor Coleridge,
"The Rime of the Ancient Mariner."

WHEN I was a boy they made me learn by heart portions of a long and, as I thought, very gloomy poem called "The Rime of the Ancient Mariner." It did not quench my attraction for the sea, but it gave me something of a prejudice against albatrosses. Birds of ill omen they seemed to me, as I struggled with this very lengthy piece of verse. Had I dared I would willingly have echoed the impatience of the wedding guest detained by the glittering eye and skinny hand of the ancient mariner— "Hold off! unhand me, grey-beard loon!" Years passed before I was able to appreciate either the magic of Samuel Taylor Coleridge or the beauty of the bird described.

When I eventually set myself the congenial task of finding out all I could about the Wandering Albatross I decided to include

an investigation of the origins of the fable upon which Coleridge
had presumably based his "Rime." It did not seem unreason-
able that the great white bird, appearing from nowhere in mid-
ocean, should have been the object of especial awe. Sailors, like
others whose lives are strongly influenced by natural pheno-
mena over which they have no control, are superstitious folk.
Stephen Fovarque in his *New Catalogue of Vulgar Errors* (1767)
says that he looks

upon our Sailors to care as little what becomes of themselves as any
set of people under the Sun, and yet no people are so terrified of an
Apparition. Their Sea Songs are full of them; they firmly believe in
their existence; and honest Jack Tar shall be more frightened at a
glimmering of the Moon . . . than he would be if a Frenchman was
to clap a Blunderbuss to his head.

Brand's *Popular Antiquities of Great Britain* (1870) speaks of the
"various puerile apprehensions" of sailors, and William Jones
in *Credulities Past and Present* (1880) remarks that

the ancient mariners performed their voyages in a vague mist of
capricious doubts and fears, omens and prognostics which excited
terror or inspired confidence. Every object which met their gaze was
endowed with some miraculous agency for good or otherwise.

James Pettitt Andrews who believed sailors to be "truly
eccentric" writes disapprovingly that

the union in sailors of the two extremes of superstition and profanity
has frequently been dwelt upon. The man who dreads the stormy
effects of drowning a cat or whistling a country dance while leaning
over the gunwhale, will too often wantonly defy his Creator by dar-
ing execrations and the most licentious behaviour.*

The early records of mankind make it plain that birds have
always been a special object of superstition in all ages and countries. The Ibis was venerated by the ancient Egyptians. In
every Roman camp was an *Augurale*, a place where the Augur
in his white robe went to read the heavens, taking special note
of the flight and song of birds. Milton in his *Astrologaster* (1620)

* *Anecdotes &c, Antient and Modern, with Observations,* 1790.

16. "Instead of the cross, the Albatross
About my neck was hung"

says of the astrologers' auguries, "They fayne that with divine instinct, birds and fowles, with their chatterings, croakings, windings, or fore-right flyings, portend either good or bad lucke." Birds, moving freely in the mysterious element of the air, were believed to search out the most carefully hidden actions of men. "No one knows except, perhaps, some bird," says the proverb.*

With this background I expected little difficulty in finding material about the albatross. Eagles, vultures, swallows, geese, magpies, crows, ravens, owls were freely mentioned. On the seafaring side I read of gannets, kingfishers, petrels, and of Rodney's famous cock which, on 12 April 1782, perched himself on the poop of the flagship and clapped his wings at every broadside poured into the French *Ville de Paris*. Still searching for something about the albatross, I found how as recently as 1857 Captain Johnson of the Norwegian barque *Ellen* behaved when a small bird flew round his head.

When the bird flew to the ship, the barque was going a little north of north-east. *I regarded the approach of the bird as an omen,* and an indication to me that I must change my course; I accordingly headed to the eastward direct. I should not have deviated from my course had not the bird visited the ship; and had it not been for this change of course I would not have fallen in with the forty-nine passengers (adrift in an open boat) whom I fortunately saved from certain death.†

There are records of other similar occurrences involving birds of various kinds, but *none* that I have found concerning the albatross. Henry Ellis's revised edition of Brand's *Popular Antiquities* has a section headed "Omens among Sailors." He deals with whistling, drowning cats, carrying corpses, losing mops and "the appearance of the Dolphin and the Porpesse . . . far from being esteemed . . . for their boundings, springs, and frolick in the water, are held to be the sure signs of an approaching Gale," but has nothing about the albatross. Dr Angelo S. Rappoport ‡ tells of enchanted islands, mermen and mermaids, phantom

* Aristophanes, *The Birds*, 414 B.C. † *Credulities Past and Present.*
‡ *Superstitions of Sailors*, 1929.

ships and apparitions, omens and ceremonies, but ignores the albatross. Only Jones, whose book was published in 1880, eighty-two years after the appearance of the *Lyrical Ballads* which included the famous "Rime," makes a passing and unsubstantiated reference to a superstition that an albatross hovering about a ship brings continued bad weather and to kill it brings bad luck.

I was beginning to have my suspicion that it was Coleridge who had invented the whole thing.

There is certainly no evidence that sailors have the slightest compunction in killing an albatross. Sparrman, who sailed with Captain Cook, writes on 12 March 1775 how "a few albatrosses and petrels were shot as a necessary treat for our table." I doubt if the albatrosses were much of a treat. The flesh of an old bird is reported as being exceedingly tough, nearly black and having a very rank, oily flavour of stale fish, "quite uneatable to the ordinary person. French sailors, however, with the culinary aptitude of their nation, hang it until it is nearly putrid, and then make stews of it, which they profess to find excellent." *

"Fishing" for albatrosses when sailing-ships were moving slowly in light winds was often indulged in and large numbers of birds were caught, as recorded by Sparrman and many others. Green (1887) gives details of the tackle used—a light, but very strong line with corks at intervals to keep it on the surface was secured to a floating bait, such as a lump of mutton fat, in which treble hooks or a simple triangle of metal had been concealed. As in other forms of fishing there must be no "drag" on the bait, the line being paid out to keep it stationary on the water until it is swooped on and seized by the bird. The line must then be kept taut, to wedge the triangle or hooks into the albatross's beak. A tug-of-war now ensues, the bird which has alighted to feed throwing back its head, pushing out its great feet and flapping its wings "full astern," and it is sometimes as much as two men can do to haul the reluctant albatross aboard. When the bird is safely on deck the tension is released. The

* *Creatures of the Sea.*

albatross drops the bait, but cannot rise from so restricted a space, even when it has "lightened ship" by bringing up the contents of its stomach, which is likely to be its first greeting to its new shipmates. It used to be thought that the birds were sea-sick, but it is clear that the reaction is the instinctive one of increasing manoeuvrability when danger threatens, for if further bothered it will next eject its oil, in considerable quantities. Green believed that in gales albatrosses use this oil to "calm the troubled waters" and logically explains that "in this their new danger, by the same manoeuvre that has so often helped them before they hope to ensure safety." It is again an instinctive reaction.

Charles Baudelaire, sailing round the Cape to Bourbon Island (Réunion) in 1841, watched the men of the crew catching albatrosses and vividly described, in his poem *L'Albatros,** the contrast between "ces rois de l'azur" and the clumsy, almost helpless birds pitifully trailing their great white wings on deck.

Nevertheless if left alone these fearless birds very soon regain their poise, "strutting and swaggering about," † though still somewhat put out by the undignified manner of their arrival aboard and not quite as amiable as usual. Scoresby ‡ describes how an albatross was set on by a very active terrier, but the bird, "though little adapted for rapid movement on deck, soon gave the dog an impressive lesson by seizing him by the nose and biting him so severely that he ran off howling most piteously." The Danish Deep Sea Expedition vessel *Galatea* had no less than twenty-two Wandering Albatrosses walking about the quarterdeck one day, "to the great amusement of the whole ship," and a photograph shows them looking calm and very much at home. They had been caught, quite uninjured, in the Tasman Sea, using a metal triangle in the bait which wedged in the curved tips of their bills.

* *Les Fleurs du Mal.*   † Green.
‡ Rev. W. Scoresby, D.D., F.R.S., *Journal of a Voyage to Australia and Round the World for Magnetical Record,* 1859.

Although the birds are not generally regarded as edible they were prized for the things which could be made out of them. Green tells us how, in ingenious hands,

webbed feet make capital tobacco pouches by drawing out all the bone and leaving the claws as ornaments.

The [hollow] wing-bones make excellent pipe stems.

The breast, if carefully cured, a warm though somewhat conspicuous muff.

The beak, in the hands of a skilled artificer, a handsome paperclip.

The killing of the birds for such purposes had at least some justification, but the shooting of albatrosses following the ship— a "sport" frequently indulged in during the nineteenth century seems a particularly wanton act. The Reverend W. Scoresby, sailing from London to Melbourne in the *Royal Charter* in 1856 to make his observations of the world's magnetic field, says that this was a "prevalent usage in many ships . . . voyaging to Australia." The American poet Edward Rowland Sill, who sailed round the Horn in 1862 in the clipper ship *Sierra Nevada*, writes feelingly of the "murder of the innocents." An account of *A Boy's Voyage Round the World* edited by Samuel Smiles (1871) tells how "some of the passengers carry on shooting at the numerous birds from the stern of the ship," adding that "such sport seems cruel, if not cowardly." This writer adds the interesting detail that the captain of the full-rigged ship *Yorkshire* was "rather displeased" when a passenger caught and killed a Mother Carey's chicken (storm-petrel), "the sailors having a superstition about these birds, that it is unlucky to kill them."*

Smiles has previously described the fishing for and killing of a number of albatrosses, but makes no mention of any superstitious fears on this account, merely remarking that the doctor's cabin, which was being used as a dissecting-room, was "like a butcher's shop . . . whilst the clergyman, who occupied the same cabin, held his handkerchief to his nose, and regarded

* "Mother Carey" is thought to be a corruption of "Mater Cara", an appellation of the Blessed Virgin Mary.

the debris of flesh and feathers on the floor with horror and dismay."

No, in the face of all this evidence it is perfectly clear that sailors have never had the smallest compunction in killing albatrosses. Why then did Coleridge suggest so strongly in his famous poem that they did?

Luckily the poet's thought-processes have been fully analysed by John Livingston Lowes in what the author calls "A Study of the Ways of the Imagination." * Documents from various sources enable him to describe in considerable detail how the "Rime" came into being. How Coleridge, drawing on what he had read and heard and on his own wonderful imagination, wove the whole into his epic poem. As an instance, Lowes believes that the idea of a man left all alone in a ship too great for him to sail single-handed, but coming safe to port, comes from a fourth-century epistle of Paulinus, Bishop of Nola, in which was told how an old man, working a pump and left behind in a ship abandoned by its crew, came, both he and his vessel unharmed, twenty-three days later to the Lucanian shore—a feat paralleled 1,500 years later by the Ancient Mariner. But it is on the matter of the albatross that Lowes is most illuminating.

In the autumn of 1797 Coleridge, with his friend Wordsworth and Wordsworth's sister Dorothy, set off on a walking tour along the Quantock Hills. Their funds were very low and, to defray the costs of the expedition, Coleridge and Wordsworth decided to write a poem. Coleridge mentioned how another friend, a certain Mr Cruikshank, had dreamt of a phantom ship, manned by skeletons. Wordsworth suggested that some crime should have been committed aboard, bringing spectral persecution. A few days earlier he had been reading a book from his library published in 1757—*A Voyage Round the World by the Great South Sea* by Captain George Shelvocke, in which the shooting of an albatross is described.

"Suppose," said Wordsworth, "you represent him [the Ancient Mariner] as having killed one of these birds on entering

* John Livingston Lowes, *The Road to Xanadu.*

the South Sea, and the tutelary spirits of these regions take upon them to revenge the crime." *

Coleridge, his imagination thoroughly stimulated, now took over, and the "Rime" as it eventually appeared in 1798 was entirely his own. He had always been profoundly interested in the occult and supernatural. He was Devon born, with the sea in his blood. He was (in his own words) "and ever have been, a great reader . . . *deep* in all out of the way books . . . accounts of all the strange phantasms that ever possessed 'your philosophy.' " † The daemons which he had studied in books on ancient cults and primitive religions were said sometimes to take the form of birds. To instal such a spirit in the albatross which

> . . . every day, for food or play,
> Came to the mariner's hollo!

was an easy step.

But what of Shelvocke, who, more than anyone else, started off this long train of thought? On 13 February 1719 the *Speedwell* left England to sail round the world. The map in Captain Shelvocke's book plots her course south and west towards the Horn.

From the latitude of forty degrees, to the latitude of fifty-two degrees we had sight of continual shoals of seals and penguins and were constantly attended by Pintado birds ‡. . . these were accompanied by Albitrosses, the largest sort of sea-fowl we know of, some of them extending their wings to a width of twelve, or thirteen feet.

The *Speedwell* ran into the usual heavy weather south of the Horn. Shelvocke writes how, on 1 October 1719

we were . . . subject to continuous squalls of sleet, snow and rain and the heavens were perpetually hidden from us by heavy and dismal clouds. In short one would imagine it impossible that any thing living could subsist in so rigid a climate, and indeed we all observed, that we had not a sight of one fish of any kind, since we were come

* Note dictated by Wordsworth to Miss Isabella Fenwick in 1843.
† A letter from Coleridge to John Thelwall, 19 November 1796.
‡ Cape Pigeons. A common southern hemisphere petrel.

to the Southward of the Straits of Le Mair; nor of one sea-bird, *excepting a disconsolate black Albitross*, who accompanied us for several days, and hovered about us as if he had lost himself, till Hatley (my second captain) concluding, in a gloomy fit, that the company of this melancholy bird brought us ill luck; resolved to destroy him in the hopes we might then have better weather, and more favourable winds than we had hitherto had to deal with in these remote, tempestuous seas. I must own that the navigation here is truly melancholy, and it was the more so to us, who were a single ship, and by ourselves in this vast and dreadful solitude.

The hot-tempered Hatley, who had already proved something of a trial to Captain Shelvocke, duly carried out his threat, but there is nothing in the record of the days immediately following to indicate that his act had, or was considered to have, any particular effect on the fortunes of the *Speedwell*. Three weeks later, on October 22, the fore-topmast carried away. Another topmast was rigged and the little ship continued to battle with contrary winds until November 14, when "at noon [they] saw the coast of Chili." Shelvocke adds that since passing through the Straits of Le Mair in September "we have been continually distressed by winds and discouraged by the weather." He makes, however, no special mention of the "Albitross."

I conclude that the belief of ill-luck attending the killing of an albatross, on which I was reared and which has gained wide credence, has no origin in the many fables of the sea. "The Rime of the Ancient Mariner" is a work of pure imagination, as Coleridge himself has called it in *Table Talk* published on 31 May 1830.

Whatever the facts may be it was the genius of Coleridge which immortalised the albatross, so let the last word be with him—

> And I had done a hellish thing,
> And it would work 'em woe:
> For all averr'd I had killed the bird
> That made the breeze to blow.
> Ah wretch! said they, the bird to slay,
> That made the breeze to blow!

4. *Flight*

IT is a typical Southern Ocean day in the Roaring Forties. The wind is blowing strongly from the west—7 to 8 on the Beaufort Scale, or 35 to 42 m.p.h. Ashore we should call it a very high wind. Trees would be swaying and bending, women would be clutching their skirts and those who wear hats would be holding them on their heads. Here it is just an average sort of a day. The sea, rolling eastward at about 20 m.p.h., has not yet risen with the wind, but there is a long swell left over from a recent gale. The waves are 100 yards from crest to crest with troughs some 15 feet deep, and our ship, steaming southward with the wind and sea on the beam, is rolling heavily. A single Wandering Albatross is in company, and as I come on deck it is some 55 feet up on the starboard quarter, just to windward of the broad lane of disturbed water spread by our passage over the heaving waves astern. The bird is overtaking us rapidly, but as I watch it turns downwind across the wake, "reefs" its wings into a shallow W and dives rapidly to leeward. Moving fast through the air and with the wind behind it, its speed over the water is very high and in a few seconds it is well to leeward; turning south and vanishing in a trough between the waves as it banks steeply just above the sea.* A few seconds later it emerges several hundred yards away on the port beam, facing the wind on fully extended wings and rising. This leg of its flight-track, against the wind, takes rather longer, but the albatross has soon crossed the wake again, turned south on to the same course as the ship and is back in its original position 55 feet up on the starboard quarter. For over an hour I watch the albatross, flying on this same curved flight-path and returning at perfectly regular intervals to the same position. Not once do I see it flap its wings. How does the bird regain the height it loses in its downward swoop to water level, and why is it not swept bodily away to leeward?

Old mariners watching albatrosses behaving in this way had quaint theories to account for what seemed like a defiance of the laws of nature. Many birds, as they knew, have internal air-sacs communicating with their lungs. The air in these sacs would be warmer, and lighter, than the air outside and some believed that the albatross, its sacs fully distended, could float along like a balloon. Unfortunately a simple calculation showed that sacs over a thousand times the size of the bird would be needed to give it the necessary buoyancy. It had been established that buzzards and other birds used rising air currents to soar over the land, and it was next supposed that the wind over the sea had enough upward direction to provide the albatross with similar lift. It is true that speed differences in the upper and lower layers give the wind a small upward slant, but the angle was found to be totally insufficient to provide continuous support. How then did the albatross sail to windward and regain lost height?

The famous glider pilot, Philip Wills, has said that the world contains two types of minds—those who wonder why the bath-water always spins out of the plug-hole the same way round, and those who don't.† This chapter is for the wonderers.

* For an albatross with a wing spread of 10 feet which banks at 70° or 80° in a sharp turn "just above the sea" is some 5 feet up.

† On Being a Bird, 1953.

The albatross is, of course, capable of powered flight, but it is as a glider, or rather as a sailplane, that it is so remarkable a creature. Man has learnt a good deal about glider design in recent years. If we start by applying this knowledge to the build and behaviour of the albatross we should discover a lot about the bird. First let us consider the constructional details of a typical sailplane and see how its lay-out compares with that of a Wandering Albatross.

The motive power of the sailplane is the force of gravity and it must use this power to the best advantage, travelling forward as far as possible with the minimum loss of height. The wings must therefore give the required support or lift with the minimum drag, or resistance to forward motion. Wind-tunnel experiments backed by practical experience have proved that long, narrow, tapered wings give the best results. The aspect ratio—the ratio between the average chord or width of the wing and its span or length—must be high. This aspect-ratio in a typical high-performance sailplane is around 18—the same as that of the Wandering Albatross. The lift/drag ratio of such a wing may be as high as 40 to 1, that is to say that for every 40 pounds of lift acting upwards at right angles to the wing there is a resistance to forward motion of one pound pulling to the rear.*

Even with the best modern materials and technique it is not easy to build a sailplane with such long and narrow wings and with the required lightness and strength. Nature in the albatross has solved the problem, notably by providing the bird with hollow wing-bones filled with air instead of marrow. The bones of a bird are very strong for their weight. The complete skeleton of an albatross weighing 20 pounds scales well under three pounds, including the breast-bones, back, head, neck, beak, skull, legs and feet.

Scientific studies extending over many years have determined the best section and form for the sailplane's wing and the wing

* The addition of fuselage and control surfaces bring the overall L/D ratio of such a sailplane down to about 30 to 1.

loading which gives the highest lift/drag ratio. In a sailplane the dimensions and form used must be a compromise, as the best shape and size for low speeds is different from that required at high speeds. Here the bird has a great advantage over the machine. Its wing is a living entity; the bones are rigid, but the feathers and joints are controlled by muscles and can be moved, allowing a wide variation in the shape and area of the wing in flight. Watch a flying albatross through glasses and you will see that not only the span of the wings, but their camber, sweep-back and dihedral (the angle at which they are held relative to the lateral axis of the bird's body) are constantly being changed. By opening or closing the feathers fan-wise the area of the wing is also being adjusted, allowing the bird to fly at something like the optimum lift/drag ratio whatever its speed.

Drag is the great enemy; it uses energy unproductively. Drag must be reduced to a minimum, not only in the wings but elsewhere as well. The fuselage of a sailplane is smooth and very carefully streamlined. Nature has endowed the albatross with a beautifully shaped body covered with overlapping feathers which give an outward form free from obstruction. Head, neck and legs blend into the body-shape in flight and the very important junction of the wings with the body is effected in a series of smooth curves. Judged by the most exacting modern standards the albatross is a splendid sailplane, but no man-made sailplane could emulate the performance of the bird, floating above the stormy seas where it lives out its wandering existence, and maintaining, with very little muscular effort, its ceaseless search for food.

A bird or a sailplane gliding through the air is continually overcoming drag; dissipating energy from the store made available by the glider's weight, height and speed. To glide at a constant or increasing speed, height must be sacrificed; that is to say the glider must be going "downhill" through the air-stream in which it moves. By seeking out places where this air-stream is moving upwards the sailplane pilot maintains or gains height. Such upward currents are to be found on the windward side of

E

hills, in "thermals" where warm air heated by the sun is rising from the ground and in "standing waves"—where air passing over a range of hills dips down on the lee side and rebounds in a series of waves—the same sort of waves as are seen behind a submerged rock in a shallow, fast-flowing river. The first and last types of lift are available in some degree above the great waves of the ocean—upward-flowing air on the flanks of the waves when the wind is moving faster or slower than the swell and air rebounding on the lee side of the crests. Instinct tells the albatross where such up-currents are to be found and it is adept at using them, but they are too irregular and operate too near the surface to give the bird the sustained lift it requires for continuous flight. There is, of course, the slight upward direction of wind over the sea already referred to, but this also is insufficient for the purpose. The albatross flies as it does by exploiting the power of the wind in quite another way.

Wind blowing over the sea is slowed down by friction. Throw a stack of playing-cards on to a table and they will spread out. The bottom card, in contact with the table-top, moves slowest over the shortest distance, the top card fastest and furthest and the remainder at intermediate speeds, determined by the

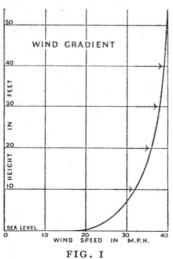

amount they are held back by friction with the slower-moving card immediately below. Wind blowing over water behaves in much the same way. If the speed of the wind is (say) 40 m.p.h. 55 feet up, it may be only 20 m.p.h. close above the surface. If we could measure the speed of the wind up to a height of 55 feet and if we made a graph, plotting wind speed against height, the result will look something like Fig. 1. The bottom layer of air is held back

FIG. I

by friction with the water, and as we go upwards each succeeding layer is slowed by friction with the slower-moving air below. Now back to the albatross.

A bird gliding *in still air* on outstretched wings at 55 feet with an air speed of 30 m.p.h. starts a dive towards the water using the force of gravity to increase its speed and levelling out just above the surface when flying at about 48 mp.h.* It immediately starts to climb, converting the extra energy it has gained in the dive back into height. When it has risen to (say) 45 feet it will have used up this surplus energy. Its air speed has now fallen away to 30 m.p.h., it has lost 10 feet of height and must now start gliding down again. The next upward swoop brings it only to (say) 32 or 35 feet; and so on, in gradually diminishing upwards curves until it must flap its wings or settle on the water. Evidently there is no future in this type of effortless flight for our albatross.

Now take the same bird, gliding at 30 m.p.h. air speed 55 feet up, not in still air, but before the wind. The wind is blowing over the sea at 40 m.p.h. at this height and at 20 m.p.h. immediately above the surface, with intermediate velocities as in Fig. 1. The albatross starts a dive exactly as before. *In still air* it would reach an air speed of 48 m.p.h. at the surface, but the bird is gliding downwind. As it dives, it enters layers of air which are moving ever more slowly over the water. In consequence the air speed of the bird builds up more rapidly, and by the time the albatross reaches the surface will be much higher than before. At these higher speeds there is rather more "drag" resisting the motion of the bird through the air, but even allowing for this the albatross will have attained an air speed of 67 m.p.h. when it levels off just above the sea (20 m.p.h. faster than before, due to the lower surface wind velocity minus 1 m.p.h. because of increased drag) (see Fig. 2 (*b*)).†

* Fig. 2, Curve (a). But for drag losses the speed would be exactly 50 m.p.h.

† For obvious reasons my graphs are not based on scientifically accurate data, but I believe them to be sufficiently exact for the purpose.

E 2

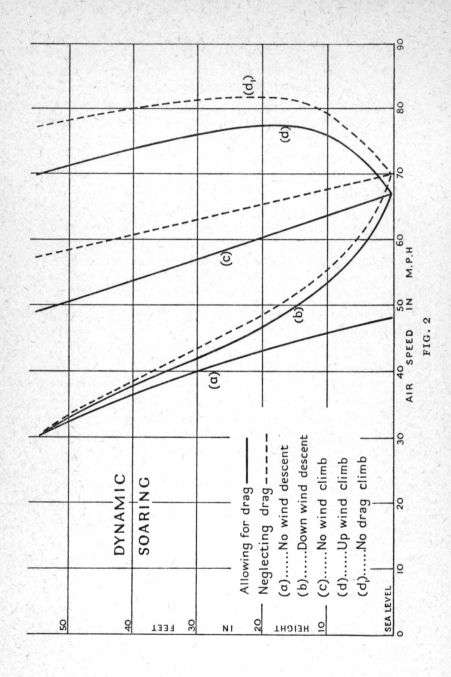

DYNAMIC
SOARING

Allowing for drag ———
Neglecting drag — — —
(a)......No wind descent
(b)......Down wind descent
(c)......No wind climb
(d)......Up wind climb
(d₁)...No drag climb

(a)
(b)
(c)
(d)
(d₁)

50
40
30
20
10
SEA LEVEL
HEIGHT   IN   FEET

0   10   20   30   40   50   60   70   80   90
AIR   SPEED   IN   M.P.H

FIG. 2

An albatross skimming along at an air speed of 67 m.p.h. has a lot of surplus energy—more than enough to enable the bird to soar back to its original height of 55 feet before its air speed drops away to 30 m.p.h. (Fig. 2 (c)), provided it is in still air or climbs across the wind gradient. This is a considerable improvement on the first state of affairs, but still not good enough for following a ship, for the bird in its dive has been moving downwind at very high *ground* speeds (up to 87 m.p.h.

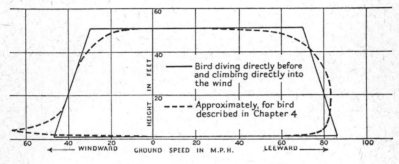

FIG. 3

when air speed and wind speed are added together) and has made considerable leeway, which must be regained.

Luckily the albatross, when it begins its upward swoop, is not in still air, but has turned into the wind, which is blowing over the sea at varying speeds as in Fig. 1. As the bird rises it is constantly entering *faster*-moving layers of air. Its air speed does not fall away as in curve (c) (the still-air curve), but is as in curve (d).* At 30 feet the albatross has an air speed of over 75 m.p.h. and it reaches 55 feet not at 30 but at 70 m.p.h. It has been moving much faster over the ground to windward all the way up, is still moving against the wind at the top of the climb and has regained all the leeway lost in the dive.

If the reader is still with me, we can now go back to the typical Southern Ocean scene at the beginning of the chapter,

* But for increased drag due to higher speed, climbing curve would be as d1.

applying the data from Figs. 1, and 2 to the flight first described.

At the highest point of its flight-curve the bird has an air speed of 30 m.p.h. It turns downward and dives towards the sea, descending at a steady angle of descent but gaining air speed rapidly because of the successively slower-moving layers of air into which it flies. At 20 feet its air speed is 46 m.p.h.; the wind directly behind it is blowing at 36 m.p.h., giving a ground speed of 82 m.p.h. to leeward. The bird now begins to turn across the wind, diving into a trough between the waves and

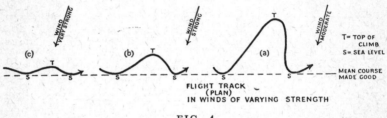

FLIGHT TRACK
(PLAN)
IN WINDS OF VARYING STRENGTH

FIG. 4

finishes its downward trajectory with an air speed of 67 m.p.h. but moving to leeward at the same speed as the sea, 20 m.p.h. Fig. 3 shows the ground speed to windward and to leeward.

The bird, using any up-currents it finds on the flanks of the waves, flies for some distance along the trough, banks and turns rapidly into the wind, using the strong up-draught near the crest of a wave to gain considerable height—an initial kick-off, as it were, of 10 or 15 feet. Its air speed instead of dropping actually rises as, propelled by its own momentum, it suddenly meets the faster-moving wind, and it forges quite rapidly to windward as it begins its steady upward climb, moving continually into layers of higher wind speed. At 20 feet its air speed is still over 77 m.p.h. and its speed to windward 41 m.p.h. At 30 feet its air speed is 75–76 m.p.h. and it is still moving steadily to windward at about 38 m.p.h. By keeping a fairly steady air speed the surplus energy accumulated in the dive is used to gain height. It finishes the upward climb with an air

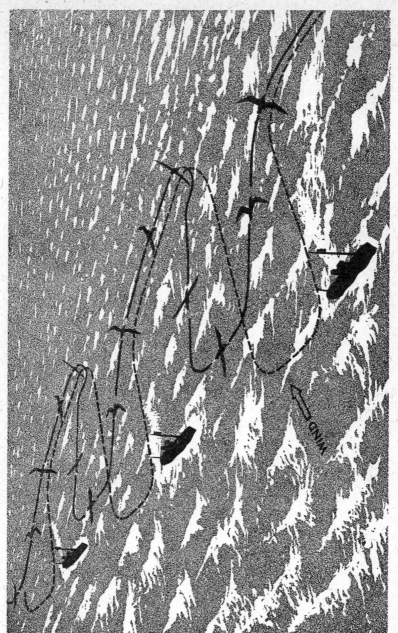

SHIP, SEA, WIND AND BIRD

speed of 65–70 m.p.h., still forging slightly to windward as it turns across the wind, and regains its position above the starboard quarter of the ship without having lost height or making any leeway. Fig. 4 shows that its average ground speed to windward on the upward slant is considerably lower (about 39 m.p.h.) than the average ground speed to leeward in the dive (around 78 m.p.h.), but this is compensated for by the fact that the dive is completed in a much shorter *time* than the climb, so that all the ground lost to leeward is eventually regained on the windward leg.

The cycle described is a typical one, susceptible to a very large number of variations, according to the strength of the wind, state and direction of the sea, mean course followed by the albatross in its search for food and so on. The principle followed is in all cases the same, the bird making only incidental use of the rising air currents close above the waves and the small upward component of the wind and relying on the *variations* in wind speed for sustained flight.

Scientifically accurate data about the flight of any bird are almost impossible to collect. You cannot make a live bird fly in a wind-tunnel nor force it to follow a prepared track along which measuring instruments have been set up. Records of the movements of birds in flight and of the surrounding air are susceptible to considerable error. The difficulties are greatly increased for sea-birds like the albatrosses, moving fast over great waves through air which, in its lower levels, is as turbulent as the stormy sea below.

In 1924 a very careful field study was carried out by Professor P. Idrac of the École Polytechnique, Paris, using automatic cameras taking photographs every 1/10th of a second and smoke-floats and anemometers to measure the direction and velocity of the wind. It was Professor Idrac who first established the now generally accepted theory of the albatross's flight which I have endeavoured to explain. In his conclusions, given in a paper read before the French Academy of Sciences and published in *Comptes Rendus* in 1924, he stated *inter alia*:

1. That only birds which are aerodynamically very "clean" and which can fly at high air speeds can keep aloft in this way. High speed is essential to build up plenty of kinetic energy in the downward dive. The energy accumulated varies with the square of the speed, i.e. it is *four* times as much at 60 m.p.h. as at 30 m.p.h.

2. Albatrosses * usually fly at air speeds varying between 35 and 85 feet per second, 30·6 and 57·8 m.p.h. Their mean air speed is about 60 feet per second, 40·8 m.p.h. They fly in a comparatively shallow layer of air extending from sea level to about 45 feet, though this maximum height is exceeded when the wind is giving greater differences between the "free" and surface winds and providing more assistance from eddies and up-draughts close above the waves.

3. The complete flight-cycle is often very regular, with an elapsed time, summit to summit, varying by as little as one second, proving that there is little dependence on the highly *irregular* air currents and eddies around the waves.

4. Soaring flight without wing-beating is possible only if the minimum wind velocity at sea level is more than 18 feet per second—11·5 m.p.h.

5. The trajectory of the bird is adjusted according to the strength of the wind and its direction relative to the mean course followed, i.e. the course produced by plotting the position of the bird at the same point on each complete flight cycle. As the wind strengthens the trajectory changes from (a) through (b) to (c) (Fig. 4), and when the wind at sea level reaches 50 feet per second (43 m.p.h.) the bird must make leeway, unless it can find an area of slower-moving air in which to fly, e.g. in the eddies and up-draughts close to a ship.

Mankind's efforts at soaring flight in his most modern sailplanes helped by the best instruments he can devise seem clumsy when compared with the natural performance of this great bird. Its instinctive knowledge of meteorology, aero-dynamics and applied mechanics is as marvellous as its split-second reactions

* Idrac included the smaller albatrosses.

to the constantly changing conditions, particularly in the highly turbulent air around the waves. One of the greatest of glider pilots, Philip Wills, has admitted that a man-carrying sailplane even with a wing-span as low as 30 feet would be far too cumbersome to operate in such a shallow layer of constantly varying air, and it seems unlikely that man will ever be able to emulate the albatross, except in his imagination.

5. *At Sea*

ALL through the summer and early autumn young birds leave the islands where they were hatched nine to twelve months before and disappear over the sea. When they first found their wings their journeys in search of food were short ones, but instinct now drives them forth to seek a living from the vast expanses of the Southern Ocean. They had been returning to the familiar breeding ground every night, but now, as the top of the island drops below the horizon astern, it is probably the last bit of land they will see for several years. Nothing daunted, the rather gawky young birds keep on over the usually stormy sea, riding the strong westerlies or resting on the water in the rare periods of comparative calm.

In spite of hundreds of specimens of the Wandering Albatross taken by ships in many parts of what Captain Dixon called the "albatross latitudes," and thousands of sighting reports covering many years, we are still without much scientifically proven knowledge of this phase of their existence. Very little ringing has been done and it is impossible to follow the fortunes of individual birds. All we can be sure about are certain general trends.

75

Even the many sighting records are slightly misleading, for they include all the "great" albatrosses and do not distinguish between the largest sort of Wandering Albatross bred in the southern part of the sub-Antarctic zone, *Diomedea exulans exulans*, and the slightly smaller birds from a little further north, *Diomedea exulans dabbena*,* sometimes known as the Tristan Wandering Albatross, which breeds on the Tristan da Cunha group, Gough Island and in the New Zealand area. The two races mingle at sea and frequent some of the same waters as the Royal Albatross, *Diomedea epomorphora*, which breeds in the southern part of South America and on islands in the Australian and New Zealand seas. Royal Albatrosses are predominantly white at all ages and can only be positively identified from old Wandering Albatrosses in the chionoptera plumage by the construction of the bill and narial tubes—a detail undistinguishable at any distance. Luckily, as the taking of specimens has proved, Royals never move far from their breeding grounds. It is only the well-named Wandering Albatross which is truly pelagic, visiting every part of the enormous zone covered by the records. Reports of white birds in areas which both Royals and Wanderers frequent are suspect, but this is a trifling percentage of the great mass of data available.

From the breeding sites the young birds spread out all over the albatross latitudes—30 million square miles, or ten times the area of the U.S.A. They lead a strange, solitary life. A ship, stirring up the surface water, a dead whale, promising rich meals of the oily morsels they love or other unusual additions to their normal food supply, will bring them together for a while, but most of the time they patrol alone, each one rapidly scanning a separate area of restless water. In twenty-seven years at sea Captain Dixon only twice saw Wandering Albatrosses congregating in large numbers, fifty near Tristan da Cunha and forty near the Crozet Islands—in both cases in the breeding season and in the vicinity of their nesting sites. Only twenty-

* Named after the distinguished Argentine ornithologist Dr Roberto Dabbene.

five times in as many years did he see ten together. Even with
his ship to attract them he found that "three or four is about the
average number seen at once, and there are a great number of
instances when the birds [are] seen alone." * A curious exception to this rule is reported by Murphy † who on 26 November
1912, and 26 March 1913 saw Wandering Albatrosses collected
in what the whalers call a "gam." On both occasions there was
no wind, the sea was comparatively calm and the birds were
sitting on the water in a large flock.

At sea Wandering Albatrosses are usually many miles apart.
A ship underway in the albatross latitudes will collect a few
birds astern during the day, but not all of them remain for long
and most drop away during the night. This habit of following
ships, stronger in the albatross than any other bird, makes it
comparatively easy to establish how many of them are in any
given area. So large a bird will certainly be seen if it approaches
within a mile, and the ship will be visible to an albatross seven
to ten miles away. Birds well to leeward may not close her if the
wind is strong, but their habits suggest that the majority up-
wind and close to leeward will come in to scan the wake, so that
the ship acts as a sort of magnet drawing the birds from a strip
eight or ten miles wide.‡

The albatross smells as well as sees its food. Hutton believes
that the tubed nostrils of the *tubinares* denote a keen sense of
smell, to compensate them for poor night vision,§ and dissection
of their heads has shown that the olfactory organs are highly
developed. The American zoologist, R. H. Beck, proved by
experiment that albatrosses and petrels can be drawn to a ship
by laying a trail of animal fat on the sea and that hot grease is
far more effective than cold, a fact which he ascribes to their
ability to follow a scent.||

* *Observations on Albatrosses and other Birds.*
† *Oceanic Birds of South America*, Vol. I.
‡ They are fond of tit-bits. The Ancient Mariner's Albatross which
"ate the food it ne'er had eat" was a thoroughly orthodox bird.
§ *Notes on Birds inhabiting the Southern Ocean.*
|| Alec A. Chisholm, *Bird Wonders of Australia.*

Assuming that most of the albatrosses patrolling near the track of a ship will be sighted, Dixon, from his careful records covering a quarter of a century, calculated the average concentration of birds in each 1,000 square miles at various seasons of the year. The highest figures he quotes are 167 in the South Atlantic, 136 west of the coast of Chile and 135 south of the Cape. These concentrations are exceptionally large; there are many single figure records and areas which yielded frequent sighting reports at one season would be empty of albatrosses at another. Ten birds to the 1,000 square miles would be something like an average figure when the birds are present at all.

The area over which the young albatrosses are spread, and which all the older birds frequent outside the breeding season, is roughly bounded by the parallels of 30 degrees and 60 degrees south latitude. There is land in the northern belt of this great zone—the southern parts of South America, South Africa and Australia and the whole of New Zealand—but even so it is four-fifths water. Between 40 and 50 degrees south is fourteen-fifteenths sea and between 50 and 60 degrees south only one forty-seventh of the area is land. The birds are not evenly distributed and are constantly on the move. Dixon and others have established that the area of greatest concentration travels around the globe once a year and extends over roughly half its circumference, with a centre south-east of New Zealand in the spring, off the west coast of Chile in the summer, south-west of the Cape of Good Hope in the autumn and in the middle of the Southern Indian Ocean in the winter. There are many sighting reports from beyond the northern and southern fringes of the zone. In the north birds are very rare below 25 degrees south, but are present in quite large numbers, particularly in winter, in slightly higher latitudes, where cold currents from the Southern Ocean turn northwards up the west coasts of Australia, South America and South Africa. To the south Wandering Albatrosses have been seen in as high a latitude as 68 degrees and even inside the Antarctic Circle amongst the ice-floes, but it is unusual for them to approach within 200 miles of the edge of the sea-ice ringing Antarctica. Birds sighted at the edge of the pack between November and April have probably been brought south by whaling operations, but there is also every indication that the main area of concentration moves, not only eastward with the seasons, but also north in winter and south in summer. Suitable weather conditions and an adequate food supply dictate the general trend.

There are certain areas around the Horn and the Cape where the birds are comparatively abundant throughout the year. There may be other such regions remote from any shipping route, for by far the greater part of this huge ocean zone is now very seldom visited by man. In the great days of sail, which ended in the early nineteen hundreds, ships sought out the strong westerlies below 40 degrees south for their voyages, but few vessels now cross the Southern Pacific in the fifties or the Southern Indian Ocean in the forties—main ocean highways in times past.* The records of bygone days, supplemented by the observations of whaling and scientific expeditions crossing the albatross latitudes in their voyages to and from the ice-edge, may long constitute our principal sources of information. In the circumstances Captain Dixon's careful records are particularly valuable and probably unique, covering all seasons, many years and spread across every latitude and longitude.

Albatrosses are big birds and require large quantities of food to keep them going. Sparrman, watching from the deck of Captain Cook's *Resolution*, was

inclined to lament the lot of the albatrosses, for this large species, although it has a body to maintain fifteen times larger than most

* A recent exception was H.M. Royal Yacht *Britannia* in which H.R.H. The Duke of Edinburgh sailed from New Zealand on 17 December 1956, arriving at the Falkland Islands on 3 January 1957 after calling at the South Shetland Islands. Her track covered 120 degrees of longitude (179 E. to 61 W.) between 44 and 67 degrees south latitude. Wandering Albatrosses were seen at irregular intervals, usually alone, but a group of 5 birds was sighted in 60.28 S., 57.18 W. No Wanderers were reported between 96 and 58 degrees W., but the Royal Yacht was in high latitudes, above 60 S., for practically the whole of this part of the voyage.

Procellariae, must be content to graze in the same fields of the Southern Ocean. . . . At least it has the strength to take and hold the largest tit-bits.*

"Grazing" is an apposite description. Short of some unexpected windfall it is only by covering a large area that the surface feeding albatross can collect the food it needs.

From Captain Dixon's figures each bird has a "grazing-ground" of nearly 4,000 acres of sea even when they are most highly concentrated. More usually it will be 75,000 to 100,000 acres, or about the area of the Isle of Wight.

For at least two years and probably longer the young albatrosses remain at sea, riding the wind far out of sight of land. Most creatures bred in and near the Arctic and Antarctic are slow in maturing. The incubation period of the Wandering Albatross is a lengthy one; the chicks remain in the nest longer than those of any other bird and the juveniles may well be very slow in reaching the stage when they can lay and fertilise eggs. Another member of the tube-nose family of which proven records exist, the Fulmar, does not develop an incubation patch for three or four years and cannot produce young until it is seven, eight or even nine years old.† Wilkins (1923) believes that female Wanderers breed at two years old, mating with older males, but only extensive ringing could prove the point. The cocks are probably slower in reaching maturity than the hens. Fledglings of the Royal Albatross hatched at Taiaroa Head, New Zealand, returned to the nesting site at ages varying between four and eight years, and a female bird bred for the first time in her ninth year.‡ Taking it all in all, I believe that a longish period of adolescent sterility in the Wandering Albatross is highly probable. Even if they do not breed until six or seven years old, there would be plenty of time for them to reproduce their kind in adequate numbers to ensure survival of the species, for there is every indication that the Wandering

* Anders Sparrman, *A Voyage Round the World with Captain James Cook.*
† James Fisher, *The Fulmar*, 1952.
‡ Richdale.

Albatross is a long-lived bird, and mortality amongst those which reach the adult stage is probably low, for they have no natural enemies. The average age of the Royals of Taiaroa was seventeen in 1952; * the oldest twenty-five.

Most of the birds seen at sea are in the juvenile (more dark than white), adolescent (half-white, half-dark) or middle-aged (more white than dark) plumage. Brown-black birds in the sombre dress in which they left their natal islands are not often sighted in the open ocean. The first feathers grown by the youngest birds are parti-coloured, and the dark tips soon wear away, revealing the white below and giving the bird a mottled appearance which grades quite rapidly into the typical juvenile plumage of the leopard goney (see Plate 6). Wandering alba- trosses in the beautiful chionoptera dress are always compara- tively rare and are, of course, less frequently seen in mid-ocean between October and June, when many of them are ashore raising a family, but there will always be a sprinkling of middle- aged birds (more white than dark) and a few old birds in the full glory of their white plumage—a fact which proves that some mature birds do not breed every year.

Experts disagree as to whether the Wandering Albatross is an annual or bi-annual breeder. If the parents have finished feed- ing their young in June (as Rankin and Murphy believe), they would have at least four months at sea free from family cares before returning to the nesting sites in November or December. If (as Matthews and Richdale contend) they continue to feed the young birds until they begin to fly there would be no such interval. Pure-white old birds and fully mature middle-aged birds more white than dark are seen at sea thousands of miles from the nearest breeding site from November to June. On the other hand, the comparative rarity of older birds in these areas during the breeding season has been noted by a number of ob- servers. The Wandering Albatross *could* breed every year after reaching maturity, but not all of them do so. The only one of the great albatrosses about which we have exact data is the

* Richdale.

Royal, and here Richdale has established that only those birds which are unsuccessful in raising a chick breed again in the following season. This rule may well apply to the Wanderer, but only extensive ringing and recapture can prove the point.

Late in the Antarctic spring some of the old and middle-aged birds receive the urge to return to the nesting sites. All over the albatross latitudes birds begin to set a course for the remote island on which they were bred. It may be hundreds or even thousands of miles away. Sailing on the wind, they cross the stormy sea, finding with unerring aim the exact spot for which they are bound and arriving, within a day or two, at exactly the same time.

When the world was very imperfectly explored and communications between distant countries non-existent, the absence of familiar birds at certain seasons of the year was put down to a number of strange causes. Hibernation in some undiscovered spot, or even a complete metamorphosis into another creature, were some of the theories advanced.

In 1703 the Reverend Charles Morton (who kept the Academy at Newington Green where Daniel Defoe received some of his early education), writing anonymously as "a person of Learning and Piety", produced an admirable little essay *Toward the Probable Solution of this Question—"Whence come the Stork and the Turtle, the Crane and the Swallow, when they know and observe the appointed Time of their Coming."*

Dr Morton rejected the possibility of swallows "lying in Clay-lumps in the bottom of rivers . . . in their sweeven and Winter Sleep" for he "never could speak with anyone who saw them so." He had noted that the arrival of migratory birds was "so sudden . . . that it is as if they were dropt down upon us from above" and concluded that they had spent their absence in the moon which he believed to have "a Composition like our Earth . . . and by consequence convenient Entertainment for these Fowls in case they arrive thither." He supported his contention by arguments which have a strangely familiar ring in this post-sputnik age. "The more remote from the Earth, the less the Gravity, and by consequence the more easy Passage; for the *Bird*, employing little or none of its strength to bear up its weight, may use it all in promotion whither it would tend . . . the Air is thin, and makes less resistance . . . therefore the whole strength of the *Bird* is reserved only for the progressive Motion . . . (which) must be abundantly more swift and easie, than it can possibly be here below in the *Atmosphere*." He allowed them two months for the journey. They would begin their flight " very Succulent and Sanguine" and live on their fat like wintering bears. They could, he believed, rest on the wing for, having "no Objects to divert them, (they) may shut their Eyes, and so swing along fast asleep, till they come to where some change of Air . . . may by its cold awake them." After two months the moon would be in the same place in the heavens as it was when they started "therefore if they proceed in a straight line, they will be sure to meet the Moon in their Way."

Since this early disquisition on space-travel the routes followed by most migratory birds, in their search for the food and weather conditions they require, have long been established, but the problem of how they find their way remains unsolved. Some believe that birds possess a sixth sense which enables them to "feel" the earth's magnetic field and steer a compass course, but pigeons released above the magnetic pole, where the lines of magnetic force give no guide, still find their way home. Others suggest that migrating birds are guided by topographical features which they recognise instinctively (the youngest birds are often the first to migrate so memory cannot come into it). Leverett Mills Loomis noted that migrating shearwaters flying over the sea were bewildered by fog, "apparently lost their bearings . . . flew about at random and . . . congregated on the water. When the shore line became visible the birds immediately resumed their journey." *

* Leverett Mills Loomis, "Remarks of the Migration of Southern Hemisphere Albatrosses and Petrels," *Auk*, Vol. XXXVIII, 1921.

Migration apart, birds which cover long distances in their search for food must "navigate," particularly over the sea. It is generally believed that they largely rely on *recognising* their surroundings. In support of this theory, Griffin and Hock of the Department of Zoology, Cornell University, carried out a number of experiments with gannets and other birds, releasing them outside their normal range and following their subsequent movements from an aircraft. Only 63 per cent of the birds found their way back. Gannets taken 100 miles inland flew around until they found some apparently familiar feature from which to set a course for home. Griffin and Hock concluded that birds do not possess any special sense of direction or sensitivity to the earth's magnetic field, but navigate by landmarks, by the direction of the prevailing wind or the bearing of the sun.*

There are differences in the colour of the water, surface disturbances caused by currents and tides and other small indications to help birds which fly over coastal waters, but purely pelagic birds like the albatross have a much stiffer problem to contend with. There are no landmarks in the open ocean, where one bit of storm-tossed sea looks uncommonly like another. The height of the sun and its bearing can certainly be used, as we use them, to determine latitude and longitude, and birds may instinctively employ this information to determine their whereabouts. It seems to me quite likely that they also use the stars, whose position in the heavens and height above the horizon are a guide not only to position, but also to the season of the year. In addition they must possess some extra sense whose nature is still a mystery. Human navigators in stormy seas, where sun and stars are sometimes hidden for days at a time, are often unaware of their exact position in spite of all their instruments, but the birds fly on unerringly. It is significant that in this terrible age of inter-continental missiles, the marvellous natural mechanism which brings a swallow from

---

* "Experiments on Bird Navigation," *Science*, Vol. 107, April 1948.

F

South Africa to the barn down the road and enables the Wandering Albatross to find a tiny island in the vast Southern Ocean is being closely studied for far less creditable purposes. If the results of these investigations enables a rocket to "home" as certainly as the starlings on Trafalgar Square, we must pray that the secret continues to elude mankind.

6. *The End and the Beginning*

SOUTH GEORGIA in early summer, and for once a calm, sunny day. The rocky mountains rise into the sky. Between them the great glaciers curve down to the edge of the sea. The island looks a little like the high Alps, submerged to above the tree-line. It is a wild, desolate place, but beautiful in its way. Between the glaciers the lower slopes of the mountains are tussock-covered. Spread over a hillside close to the rocky beach are the mounds of many old albatross nests, trampled down and mis-shapen by prolonged use by the young birds, some of which are sitting about in their black-brown plumage. Their white faces and innocent eyes give them a goofy, clownish look. Goney is a good name for the birds of this age.

Yesterday there were no old birds to be seen, but since day-light snow-white Wanderers have been coming in from the sea —male birds in the full glory of their chionoptera dress. For several days the old cocks continue to arrive. They have been at sea for a long time and have flown tens of thousands of miles. Small wonder if they land heavily and walk uncertainly. It is four or five months at least, and perhaps well over a year, since they had anything under them but air or water, and though they have often used their legs for rising from the sea, it is long since they walked on solid ground. Perhaps the tussock-covered hillside seems to rise and fall beneath their feet in the disconcerting manner which we experience after a long period afloat. Walking was, in any case, never their strongest suit.

Heads low and necks extended, they waddle to an old nest, perhaps the very one they themselves helped to build. If a gawky young goney is still in occupation it takes itself off. Mr Harris, the engineer of His Majesty's Ship *Adventure*, who was wrecked on Kerguelen in 1833, stated that the old birds went at once to their old nests and "after a little fondling of the young one" which was on or near the nest, turned it away. Harris was ashore for several months here and on Prince Edward I. and had unique opportunities for observation, but whether the returning cocks go to their old nests or simply annex one which takes their fancy is a matter for conjecture.*

For several days the old white males wander round repairing the selected nest or sit quietly upon it resting and waiting. The youngsters continue their flying practice, making short trips over the sea. It is all as peaceful as Sunday afternoon, until the ladies arrive.

No sooner has the first hen flopped on to the tussock than every cock in sight waddles towards her as fast as his clumsy gait will allow. Each female is soon surrounded by a throng of importunate suitors. The peaceful interlude is over, but even at this exciting moment strict protocol is observed, and the ritual which follows is conducted with a degree of decorum unusual in these informal days.

Each group of four or five cocks forms a ring with a hen in the centre. Hitherto quite silent, they now begin to utter harsh, groaning sounds, not unlike the braying of an ass and no more pleasant or musical. The female faces each male in turn, and the two birds perform a sort of dance in which the cock is the most active partner. It seems that he is trying to show her what

* F. W. Hutton, *Notes on Birds inhabiting the Southern Ocean.*

a splendid fellow he is, stretching to his full height on extended legs and displaying, first with his great wings half open and finally with them fully spread. At this point the male stretches his neck upwards and points his bill at the sky.

"Take a good look," he brays. "You'll never see a finer bird."

The female, who has been facing him demurely, now turns to another bird and the ritual is repeated.

The males not actively engaged continue to bow and bray, threaten one another with clappering bills and might, in their ass-like groans, be thought to be commenting pretty freely on the shortcomings of their rivals. But it is all astonishingly decorous in a bucolic sort of way, and fighting or interfering with the dance is quite beneath their dignity. If their feelings become too much for them they stroll a short distance from the ring "with their heads swaying from side to side and hung almost to the ground. The attitude gives them a diabolical look, and it would be easy to imagine that dark and sinister thoughts were occupying their minds." *

Like a good hostess at a party, the female divides her attentions very fairly between the importunate males, and not until all have displayed does she make her selection. The successful suitor shepherds his bride-to-be to his nest. Other females are constantly arriving from the sea and the rejected males, not unduly put out, waddle off to try their luck elsewhere.

It is after the birds have paired that courtship proper begins. The very elaborate ritual which now takes place is conducted on and by the nest. It so absorbs the participants that they are perfectly indifferent to the presence of spectators, and every part of the ceremony can be observed and photographed.

The scene opens with the cock sitting on the nest, the hen crouching on the ground beside him. Both birds begin to croak, opening their bills widely as they do so and making a noise which Rankin has compared to a man with a cleft palate trying to calm a restive horse. The duet continues for about a quarter

* Murphy.

of an hour. After, or sometimes during, this exchange of compliments both birds nibble at the short feathers of their partner's neck. They remain sitting, their long legs bent under them.

The male now rises to his feet, stretches his neck to the sky and utters a bubbling noise, at the same time rapidly clappering his bill, the lower mandible moving much faster than the upper and making a rattling sound. These jazz effects produce an immediate reaction. The female springs to her feet, stands bolt upright, stretches up her neck and brings her bill close to his. Drops of oil may be passed from one bird to another at this stage.

Both birds are now bubbling and clappering, sometimes bringing their beaks together and concluding each phrase (though the noise they make is far from music to our ears) with a loud snap of the bill, after which the head is lowered and the partner's breast-feathers touched, though not preened. Excitement is mounting and the dance proper is about to begin.

The male, still standing on the nest, spreads his wings in a great curve with the tips held well forward, stretches his neck vertically upwards and points his bill straight at the sky. Holding this position, he turns slowly through a full circle, lifting each great foot in turn high in the air with the measured precision of a guardsman doing a slow march. All the time he lets out a high-pitched, pig-like squeak. The female, though evidently greatly flattered, is coy. She may feign complete indifference, standing quite still, wearing what Richdale calls the gawky look. She may waddle round the nest with her neck stretched out and head held low. At most she will condescend to a decorous participation in the dance; demure and silent, facing her partner as he revolves squealing, upon the nest.

But the final crisis is fast approaching. He has wooed and all but won her. When he is facing in the direction from which he began his turn he stretches his wings to their fullest possible extent, cocks his tail upwards and shrieks to the full capacity of his lungs. No female could ignore so fervent a declaration. The hen now moves immediately in front of him, spreads her wings, lifts her bill to the sky and struts forward on straight legs until their breasts are almost touching. Mating may perhaps now take place, though quite frequently this ecstatic climax is followed by anti-climax, both birds suddenly seeming to tire of the whole performance and sinking exhausted to the ground to rest quietly side by side. Later, perhaps after a little nest-building, they will start the whole ceremony again from the beginning. The Wandering Albatross, so solitary and aloof for most of its life, is an ardent bird, and courting continues, no less fervently, whilst the nest is being prepared and even after the egg is laid.

Paired albatrosses are not always allowed to complete this elaborate ritual without interference. Unattached birds, especially importunate young females, will sometimes join in, and this, as might be expected, leads to trouble, in which the male very wisely refuses to take part. Actual fights are rare. Some small birds fight to the death, but these great creatures seem content with purely ritual combat. There is much bill-clappering and snapping until one of the ladies accepts moral defeat and takes herself off. Unpaired males rarely try their luck at this stage. Later, when the mated cock has gone foraging to sea, leaving the hen on her own, young blades are not above ogling the temporarily unescorted females. It has been averred by Wilkins (1923) that old white males left in charge of the nest by their spouses before the egg is laid will sidle up to young females and even mate with them, though Murphy believes that the Wandering Albatross mates only with its own partner after pairing. A good deal of social visiting between the birds occupying neighbouring nests certainly takes place, but he contends that it results in nothing more serious than a little neck-nibbling.

Richdale, with his unique opportunities for observation of the Royal Albatross colony at Taiaroa, has established that these birds often pair for life. Further, he believes that paired birds continue to associate when at sea. Wanderers appear to select a new mate each time they come ashore to breed, the older males showing that marked preference for sprightly young

females which has sometimes been noted in other walks
of life.

Richdale has discovered that mating between Royals takes
place twenty-seven days before the egg is laid. The exact period
for Wanderers is not known. The continuation of courtship between Wanderers during incubation and even after the young
have hatched * is a feature which has few parallels in the bird
world. New birds are continually arriving at the nesting site
from the sea, the youngest not coming ashore until February or
March, when the first birds to pair have already hatched their
eggs. Courting and mating go on throughout this period, and it
is possible that Wilkins, who casts so much doubt on the fidelity
of the Wandering Albatross, mistook the love-making of the
newly arrived youngsters for promiscuity amongst their elders.
Faithfulness to their chosen mate distinguishes many of the
higher animals, in which category I would like to include
Diomedea exulans.

So ends, and begins, the life-cycle of the Wandering Albatross. On land, as at sea, there is much dignity, even nobility,
in the behaviour of this great bird. Strong but gentle, fearless
but not aggressive, capable of great feats of endurance and
calmly surmounting the difficulties of existence in a wild and
stormy environment. Interfering very little with the affairs of
others of its kind or with the weaker species with which it shares
its range. Enjoying the social amenities of its short spells ashore,
but returning always to its ceaseless vigil above the restless sea.
For much of its long life the Wandering Albatross is alone, sailing on outstretched wings far out of sight of land. It will probably be alone when old age gradually overtakes it. What happens then? This, like much else about the Wandering Albatross, is a mystery.

* Wilkins.

Courting. 17. Conversation piece (*top*) followed by 18. neck-nibbling (*bottom*).
Cock-bird on the nest

Courting (*continued*). 19. Bubbling and bill-clappering (*top*). 20. A forward young female tries to join the dance (*bottom*)

21. Cock displaying, with wing-tips curved forward (*top*). The hen is coy. 22. With eyes only for each other (*bottom*)

23. The climax of the dance

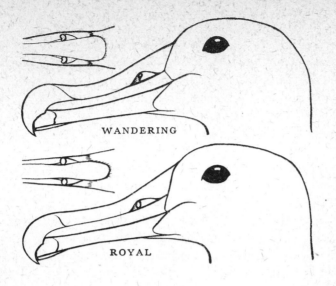

WANDERING

ROYAL

The Albatrosses

WITH SOME NOTES ON HOW TO IDENTIFY THE WANDERING ALBATROSS

ALL albatrosses belong to the Diomedeidae family of the order Procellariiformes. James Lee Peters in his *Check-List of Birds of the World*, published by the Harvard University in 1931, includes twelve species in the genus *Diomedea*, a further two in the genus *Phoebetria* and lists a total of nineteen races. In the revised edition of W. B. Alexander's *Birds of the Ocean*, published by G. P. Putnam's Sons, New York, the albatrosses include eleven *Diomedea* and two *Phoebetria*, and fifteen races.

Other experts disagree more widely on the number of different forms of albatross, and different scientific names are applied by various authorities to what Peters and Alexander regard as birds of the same race.

Peters and Alexander both agree that the Wandering Albatross, *Diomedea exulans* (Linné), has only two races *D. exulans exulans*, which breeds on S. Georgia and other islands in the Southern part of the nesting zone, and *D. exulans dabbenena*, a slightly smaller bird which breeds on Inaccessible (Tristan da Cunha Group) and Gough Islands. Synonyms of *D. exulans* include *D. chionoptera* (Salvin), *D. e. rohui* (Mathews), *D. e westralis* (Mathews), *D. chionoptera alexanderi* (Dabbene), *D. Spadicea* (Gmelin), *D. adusta* (Tschudi), *D. e. Georgia* (Mathews), and *D. e rothschildi* (Mathews).

All albatrosses except the Royal are smaller than the Wanderer, but it is not possible to identify the "great" albatrosses by their size alone—dimensions are notoriously difficult to judge at sea.

The Short-tailed Albatross, the Black-footed Albatross and the Laysan Albatross are birds of the northern hemisphere.

The Waved Albatross is confined to the tropics.

Of the nine (Peters) or eight (Alexander) species whose range overlaps that of the Wandering Albatross, two, the Sooty Albatross and the Light-mantled Sooty Albatross, have plumage which is mainly brown. So have young Wanderers, but Sooties have a dark under-surface to their wings and a wedged-shaped tail.

All but one of the remaining six (or seven) species have, like the Wanderer, bodies which are mostly white. But the middle of their backs is *always* dark and the upper surface of the wings dark even in the most adult form. Viewed from above as they bank in a turn they are a dark looking bird.

The Shy Albatross, as its name implies, rarely approaches a ship. Buller's Albatross is very rare and very much smaller than *D. exulans*. The Black-browed Albatross has a slaty streak passing through the eye which shows up clearly as the head of the bird is white. The Yellow-nosed Albatross has a black bill with a yellow line down the centre of the upper mandible, which is orange at the tip. The Grey-headed Albatross is very similar, but its head is usually grey.

This leaves only the Royal Albatross, *D. epomophora* (also known as *D. regia* and *D. sanfordi*). The plumage of these birds does not change with age and greatly resembles that of *D. exulans* in the chionoptera stage. The only certain way of

distinguishing a Royal from an old male Wanderer is by the
shape of its nostrils and its more slender bill. Royal and
Wanderers share the waters around the coast of South America,
(as far north as central Chile and Uruguay), New Zealand and
south-eastern Australia. Outside these areas an Albatross with
a white back is almost certainly a Wanderer.

Check List

	1. Wandering Albatross
	2. Royal Albatross
	3. Shy Albatross
	4. Buller's Albatross
Backs *always* dark	5. Black-browed Albatross
	6. Yellow-nosed Albatross
	7. Grey-headed Albatross
Dark under wings	8. Sooty Albatross
Wedged tail	9. Light Mantled Sooty Albatross
Tropics only	10. Waved Albatross
	11. Short-tailed Albatross
Northern hemisphere	12. Black-footed Albatross
only	13. Laysan Albatross

An albatross which nests on Desolation Island, at the western
end of the Straits of Magellan, is included by Peters as a four-
teenth species—*Diomedea desolationis*.

BIBLIOGRAPHY

ALBIN, ELEAZAR: *A Natural History of Birds*, Vol. I (William Innys, London, 1738).

ALEXANDER, W. B.: *The Birds of the Ocean* (G. P. Putnam's Sons, Revised edition, New York, 1954).

ANDREWS, JAMES PETTIT: *Anecdotes etc. Antient and Modern, with Observations*, London, 1790.

AYMAR, GORDON C.: *Bird Flight* (John Lane, The Bodley Head, 1936).

BAIRD, SPENCER F.: *The Birds of North America* (1860).

BEEBE, WILLIAM: *The Bird, Its Form and Function* (Constable, 1907).

BIERMAN, W. H., AND VOOUS, K. H.: *Birds Observed and Collected during the Whaling Expeditions of the "William Barendsz" in the Antarctic, 1946–1947 and 1947–1948* (E. J. Brill, Leiden, 1950. *Ardea* 37, Supplementary Number).

BOURNE, HENRY: *The Antiquities of the Common People* (J. White, Newcastle, 1735).

BRAND, JOHN: *Observations on Popular Antiquities* (T. Saint, Newcastle-upon-Tyne, 1777).

——: *Observations on Popular Antiquities*. Arranged and revised by Henry Ellis (London, 1813).

——: *Popular Antiquities of Great Britain* (John Russell Smith, 1870).

BREWER, EBENEZER COBHAM: *Dictionary of Phrase and Fable* (Cassell, London, 1923).

British Antarctic (Terra Nova) Expedition 1910 (*Zoology*, Vol. 4 Birds, British Museum).

BULLEN, FRANK T.: *Creatures of the Sea* (Religious Tract Society, 1904).

Catalogue of Birds in the British Museum, Vol. XXV (London, 1896).

CAYLEY, NEVILLE W.: *What Bird is That?* (Angus and Robertson, Sydney).

CHISHOLM, ALEC H.: *Bird Wonders of Australia* (Angus and Robertson, Sydney, 1943).

COLERIDGE, SAMUEL TAYLOR: *The Rime of the Ancient Mariner*. Illustrated by E. H. Wehnert, E. Duncan and Birket Foster (Sampson Low, 1857. Printed by R. Clay, Bread Street Hill).

COOK, CAPTAIN JAMES, the Circumnavigator: *A Voyage towards the South Pole and round the World* (London, 1779).

DIXON, C. C.: *Some Observations on the Albatrosses and other birds of the Southern Ocean* (Transactions of the Royal Canadian Institute, Vol. XIX, 1933).

EDWARDS, GEORGE: *A Natural History of Uncommon Birds*, Part II (Printed at the College of Physicians, 1747).

ELLIOTT, H. F. I.: *A Contribution to the Ornithology of the Tristan Da Cunha Group* (*Ibis*, Vol. 99, No. 4, 1 October 1957).

FISHER, JAMES, AND LOCKLEY, R. M.: *Sea Birds* (Collins, 1954).

FISHER, JAMES: *The Fulmar* (Collins, 1952).

FORSTER, JOHN REINOLD: *Observations Made during a Voyage Round the World* (1778).

FORSTER, J. G. A.: *A Voyage to the Cape of Good Hope* (1785).

FOVARQUE, STEPHEN, Fellow of St John's College: *A New Catalogue of Vulgar Errors* (Cambridge, 1767).

The "Galathea" Deep Sea Expedition, 1950–52. Translated from the Danish by Reginald Spink (Allen and Unwin, 1956).

GOODRIDGE, C. M.: *Narrative of a Voyage to the South Seas and the Shipwreck of the Princess of Wales cutter, etc.* (Exeter, 1841).

GOULD, JOHN: *The Birds of Australia*, Vol. VII (Published by the author, 1948).

GREEN, J. F.: *Ocean Birds* (R. H. Porter, 1887).

GRIFFIN, DONALD R., AND HOCK, RAYMOND J.: *Experiments in Bird Navigation* (*Science*, Vol. 107, 2 April 1948).

HALL, ROBERT: *Field-notes on the Birds of Kerguelen Island* (*Ibis*, Seventh Series, No. XXI, January 1906).

HARTWIG, DR G.: *The Polar World* (Longmans Green, 1869).

——: *The Sea and Its Living Wonders* (Longmans Green, 1875).

HAZLITT, W. CAREW: *Faiths and Folklore, A Dictionary*, Vol. II (London, 1905).

HORSLEY, TERENCE: *Soaring Flight* (Eyre and Spottiswoode, 1944).

HUTTON, CAPTAIN F. W.: *Remarks on the Flight of Albatrosses* (*Ibis*, Eighth Series, Vol. III, 1903).

——: *Notes on some of the Birds inhabiting the Southern Ocean* (*Ibis*, New Series, Vol. I, 1865).

IDRAC, PROFESSOR P., L'Ecole Polytechnique, Paris: *Experimental Study of the "Soaring" of Albatrosses* (*Nature*, Vol. CXV. Comptes Rendus, 1924).

JONES, WILLIAM: *Credulities Past and Present* (Chatto and Windus, 1880).

LATHAM: *A General Synopsis of Birds*, Vol. III (Leigh and Sotheby, 1785).

LOOMIS, L. M.: *Remarks on the Migration of the Southern Hemisphere Albatrosses and Petrels* (*Auk*, Vol. XXXVIII, 1921).

MATHEWS, G. M.: *Remarks on the Albatrosses and Mollymawks* (*Ibis*, Thirteenth Series, Vol. IV, 1934).

MATTHEWS, L. HARRISON: *The Birds of South Georgia* (*Discovery Reports*, Vol. I, 1929).

——: *Wandering Albatross* (MacGibbon and Kee, 1951).

——: *The Origin of Stomach Oil in Petrels* (*Ibis*, Vol. 91, 1949).

——: *South Georgia* (Simpkin Marshall, 1931).

MIGOT, ANDRÉ: *The Lonely South* (Rupert Hart-Davis, 1956).

——: *Kerguelen* (E. J., Paris, 1955).

MORTON, REV. CHARLES, ("A person of Learning and Piety"): *An Essay towards the Probable Solution of this Question, Whence come the Stork and the Turtle, the Crane and the Swallow, when they Know and Observe the Appointed Time of their Coming* (London, 1703).

MOSELEY, H. N.: *Notes by a naturalist on the "Challenger" . . . during the voyage round the world . . . 1872–1876* (Macmillan, London, 1879).

MURPHY, ROBERT CUSHMAN: *Observations on the birds of the South Atlantic* (*Auk*, Vol. XXXI, October 1914).

——: *Oceanic Birds of South America*, Vol. I (The Macmillan Company, The American Museum of Natural History, New York, 1936).

——: *Logbook for Grace* (The Macmillan Company, New York, 1948).

NUTTALL, THOMAS: *A Manual of the Ornithology of the United States, The Water Birds* (Hilliard Gray, Boston, 1834).

OLIVER, W. R. B.: *New Zealand Birds* (A. H. and A. W. Reed, Wellington, 1955).

PEMBROKE, LORD, AND KINGSLEY, DR G. H. ("The Earl and the Doctor"): *South Sea Bubbles* (Richard Bentley & Son, 1873).

PENNANT's *Arctic Zoology*, Vol. II (Henry Hughes, London, 1785).

PETERS, J. L.: *Check-list of Birds of the World*, Vol. I (Harvard University Press, Cambridge, 1931).

RANKIN, NIALL: *Antarctic Isle* (Collins, 1951).

RAPPOPORT, DR ANGELO S.: *Superstitions of Sailors* (Stanley Paul, 1929).

RICHDALE, L. E.: *The pre-egg stage in the albatross family* (Otago Daily Times and Witness Newspapers, Dunedin, 1950).

——: *Post-egg period in albatrosses* (Otago Daily Times and Witness Newspapers, Dunedin, 1952).

ROBERTS, BRIAN: *A Bibliography of Antarctic Ornithology*, British Graham Land Expedition 1934–1937 (*Scientific Reports*, Vol. I, No. 9, British Museum, London, 1941).

ROUTH, MARTIN: *Ornithological Observations in the Antarctic Seas, 1945–46* from the whale factory ship "Balaena" (*Ibis*, Vol. 91, 1949).

SCORESBY, REV. W.: *Journal of a Voyage to Australia and Round the World for Magnetical Research* (Longman, Green, Longman & Roberts, 1859).

SHELVOCKE, CAPTAIN GEORGE: *A Voyage Round the World by Way of the Great South Sea* (M. and T. Longman, 1757).

SILL, EDWARD ROWLAND: *Around the Horn* (Yale University Press, 1944).

SMILES, SAMUEL: *A Boy's Voyage Round the World* (John Murray, London, 1871).

SPARRMAN, ANDERS: *A Voyage Round the World with Captain James Cook in H.M.S. Resolution* (Robert Hale, 1953).

——: *A Voyage to the Cape of Good Hope, towards the Antarctic Circle and Round the World.* Translated by G. Forster (Second Edition, 1785).

SOMERVILLE, REAR-ADMIRAL BOYLE T.: *Ocean Passages of the World* (H.M.S.O., 1923).

SUTCLIFFE, R. C.: *Meteorology for Aviators* (H.M.S.O., 1940).

VERRILL, G. E.: *Birds and Eggs, Kerguelen Island, etc.* (Transactions of Connecticut Academy of Arts and Sciences, New Haven, Vol. IX, 1895).

Voyage of S.Y. "Scotia" 1902, –03, –04, *Ornithology of the Scottish National Antarctic Expedition*, Vol. IV Zoology, Part XIV Birds (The Scottish Oceanographical Laboratory, Edinburgh, 1915).

WEDDELL, JAMES, Master in the Royal Navy: *A Voyage towards the South Pole in the years 1822–24* (London, 1825).

WILKINS, G. H.: *Report on birds collected during the voyage of the "Quest" (Shackleton-Rowatt Expedition) to the southern Atlantic* (*Ibis*, (11), 5, 1928).

WILLS, P. A.: *On Being a Bird* (Max Parrish, 1953).

WILSON, EDWARD A.: *National Antarctic Expedition of S.S. Discovery under Captain R. F. Scott, 1904–1910* (*Aves*, British Museum, 1907).